# PRIMARY MATHEMATICS 6A

## TEXTBOOK

Marshall Cavendish
Education

Original edition published under the title Primary Mathematics 6A
© 1984 Curriculum Planning & Development Division
Ministry of Education, Singapore
Published by Times Media Private Limited
This American Edition
© 2003 Times Media Private Limited
© 2003 Marshall Cavendish International (Singapore) Private Limited
© 2014 Marshall Cavendish Education Pte Ltd

**Published by Marshall Cavendish Education**
Times Centre, 1 New Industrial Road, Singapore 536196
Customer Service Hotline: (65) 6213 9444
US Office Tel: (1-914) 332 8888 | Fax: (1-914) 332 8882
E-mail: tmesales@mceducation.com
Website: www.mceducation.com

First published 2003
Reprinted 2003, 2004
Second impression 2005
Third impression 2006
Reprinted 2007 (twice), 2008, 2009 (twice), 2010, 2011, 2012 (twice),
        2014, 2015, 2016, 2017 (twice)

ISBN 978-981-01-8514-5

Printed in Singapore

## ACKNOWLEDGEMENTS

Our special thanks to Richard Askey, Professor of Mathematics (University of Wisconsin,
Madison), Yoram Sagher, Professor of Mathematics (University of Illinois, Chicago), and Madge
Goldman, President (Gabriella and Paul Rosenbaum Foundation), for their indispensable
advice and suggestions in the production of Primary Mathematics (U.S. Edition).

# PREFACE

Primary Mathematics (U.S. Edition) comprises textbooks and workbooks. The main feature of this package is the use of the **Concrete → Pictorial → Abstract** approach. The students are provided with the necessary learning experiences beginning with the concrete and pictorial stages, followed by the abstract stage to enable them to learn mathematics meaningfully. This package encourages active thinking processes, communication of mathematical ideas and problem solving.

The textbook comprises 5 units. Each unit is divided into parts: ❶, ❷, . . . Each part starts with a meaningful situation for communication and is followed by specific learning tasks numbered 1, 2, . . . The textbook is accompanied by a workbook. The sign [ Workbook Exercise ⟩ is used to link the textbook to the workbook exercises.

Practice exercises are designed to provide the students with further practice after they have done the relevant workbook exercises. Review exercises are provided for cumulative reviews of concepts and skills. All the practice exercises and review exercises are optional exercises.

The color patch ■ is used to invite active participation from the students and to facilitate oral discussion. The students are advised not to write on the color patches.

# CONTENTS

# 1 Algebra

## 1 Algebraic Expressions

Angela and Limei make the following table to compare their ages.

| Angela's age | Limei's age |
|:---:|:---:|
| 6 | 8 |
| 7 | 9 |
| 8 | 10 |
| 9 | 11 |
| 10 | 12 |

When Angela is 12 years old, how old is Limei?

When Angela is 15 years old, how old is Limei?

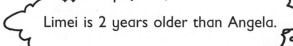

Limei is 2 years older than Angela.

When Angela is $n$ years old, Limei is $(n + 2)$ years old.

$n$ stands for any whole number.

When $n = 16$, $n + 2 = 16 + 2 = 18$

When $n = 20$, $n + 2 = $ ■

1.  Alan is 8 years old.
    (a)  How old will he be in 5 years' time?

    (b)  How old will he be in $x$ years' time?
         Give the answer in terms of $x$.

2.  Jim has $2 more than Travis.
    (a)  If Jim has $10, how much money does Travis have?

    (b)  If Jim has $$m$, how much money does Travis have?
         Give the answer in terms of $m$.

3.  Tracy bought $w$ kg of flour. She used 5 kg of it.
    (a)  Express the amount of flour left in terms of $w$.

         Amount of flour left = $(w - 5)$ kg

    (b)  If Tracy bought 8 kg of flour, how much flour did she have left?

         $w - 5 = 8 - 5 = $ ■

         She had ■ kg of flour left.

4. There are 4 apples in each packet.

(a) How many apples are there in $n$ packets?

| Number of packets | Total number of apples |
|---|---|
| 1 | $4 \times 1 = 4$ |
| 2 | $4 \times 2 = 8$ |
| 3 | $4 \times 3 = 12$ |
| 4 | $4 \times 4 = 16$ |
| 5 | $4 \times 5 = 20$ |
| $n$ | $4n$ |

We write $4 \times n$ as $4n$.

(b) If $n = 8$, how many apples are there altogether?
(c) If $n = 11$, how many apples are there altogether?

5. There are 3 boxes of chicken wings. Each box contains $p$ chicken wings.
   (a) Express the total number of chicken wings in terms of $p$.

   Total number of chicken wings = $3p$

$3p$ means $3 \times p$ or $p \times 3$.

   (b) If each box contains 7 chicken wings, how many chicken wings are there altogether?

   $3p = 3 \times 7 = \blacksquare$

   There are $\blacksquare$ chicken wings altogether.

6. A rectangular tile measures $k$ cm by 8 cm. Express its area in terms of $k$.

$k \times 8 = 8k$

7. Ali has 8 boxes. He puts an equal number of marbles in each box.
   (a) If there are 96 marbles, find the number of marbles in each box.

   Number of marbles in each box = $\dfrac{96}{8}$ = ■

   (b) If there are $x$ marbles, find the number of marbles in each box in terms of $x$.

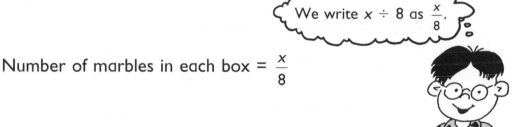

   We write $x \div 8$ as $\dfrac{x}{8}$.

   Number of marbles in each box = $\dfrac{x}{8}$

8. Meihua bought 3 books.
   (a) If the total cost of the books is $12, find their average cost.

   Average cost = $\dfrac{\$12}{3}$ = \$■

   (b) If the total cost of the books is $m, find their average cost in terms of $m$.

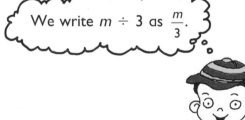

   We write $m \div 3$ as $\dfrac{m}{3}$.

   Average cost = $\dfrac{\$m}{3}$ = \$$\dfrac{m}{3}$

9. Find the value of each of the following when $n = 6$.
   (a) $n + 4$          (b) $10 + n$          (c) $15 - n$
   (d) $n - 6$          (e) $4n$              (f) $10n$
   (g) $\dfrac{n}{2}$   (h) $\dfrac{n}{6}$    (i) $\dfrac{n}{12}$

Workbook Exercise 1

10. Tyrone has some marbles. He puts $x$ marbles in a bag. There are 5 bags and 3 marbles altogether.

(a) Express the total number of marbles in terms of $x$.

x marbles in each bag.
5x marbles in 5 bags.

Total number of marbles = $5x + 3$

(b) If $x = 10$, how many marbles does Tyrone have?

$5x + 3 = 5 \times 10 + 3 =$ ■

Tyrone has ■ marbles.

11. Find the value of $2x - 3$ when $x = 5$.

$2x - 3 = 2 \times 5 - 3 =$ ■

12. Jeff had $50. He gave $$y$ to his son. The remainder was then shared equally between his two daughters.

(a) Express each daughter's share in terms of $y$.

Amount of money shared by the daughters $= \$(50 - y)$

Amount of money each daughter received $= \$\dfrac{50 - y}{2}$

(b) If $y = 12$, how much money did each daughter receive?

$$\frac{50 - y}{2} = \frac{50 - 12}{2} = \blacksquare$$

Each daughter received $■.

13. Find the value of $\dfrac{x - 4}{2}$ when $x = 12$.

$$\frac{x - 4}{2} = \frac{12 - 4}{2}$$

$$= \frac{8}{2}$$

$$= \blacksquare$$

14.    (a)   Find the value of $\dfrac{4n + 3}{5}$ when $n = 8$.

$$\frac{4n + 3}{5} = \frac{4 \times 8 + 3}{5} = \blacksquare$$

      (b)   Find the value of $\dfrac{45 - 3r}{3}$ when $r = 5$.

$$\frac{45 - 3r}{3} = \frac{45 - 3 \times 5}{3} = \blacksquare$$

15.    We write $y \times y$ as $y^2$.
      Find the value of the following when $y = 3$.
      (a)   $y^2$

$$y^2 = 3 \times 3 = \blacksquare$$

      (b)   $2y^2$

$$2y^2 = 2 \times 3 \times 3 = \blacksquare$$

      (c)   $\dfrac{y^2}{5}$

$$\frac{y^2}{5} = \frac{3 \times 3}{5} = \blacksquare$$

16.    We write $a \times a \times a$ as $a^3$.
      Find the value of the following when $a = 2$.
      (a)   $a^3$

$$a^3 = 2 \times 2 \times 2 = \blacksquare$$

      (b)   $a^3 + 1$

$$a^3 + 1 = 2 \times 2 \times 2 + 1 = \blacksquare$$

      (c)   $a^2 + a^3$

$$a^2 + a^3 = 2 \times 2 + 2 \times 2 \times 2 = \blacksquare$$

17.    Find the value of each of the following when $a = 5$.

| | | |
|---|---|---|
| (a)   $\dfrac{4a}{3}$ | (b)   $8 + 3a$ | (c)   $2a - 3$ |
| (d)   $\dfrac{a}{3} + 2$ | (e)   $\dfrac{3a - 4}{2}$ | (f)   $\dfrac{2a + 5}{5}$ |
| (g)   $2a^2 - 3$ | (h)   $a^3 + 5$ | (i)   $a^3 - a$ |

Workbook Exercise 2

18. John has 4 bags of red beads and 3 bags of green beads. There are $x$ beads in each bag.

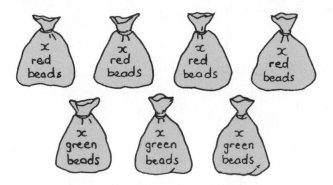

(a) Find the total number of beads in terms of $x$.

Number of red beads   = $4x$

Number of green beads = $3x$

Total number of beads   = $4x + 3x$

                               = $7x$

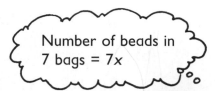

Number of beads in 7 bags = $7x$

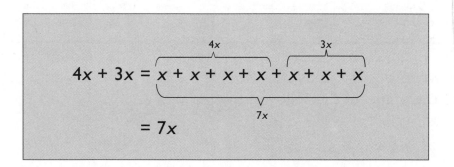

$$4x + 3x = \underbrace{\overbrace{x + x + x + x}^{4x} + \overbrace{x + x + x}^{3x}}_{7x}$$

$$= 7x$$

(b) How many more red beads than green beads are there?

$$4x - 3x = x$$

There are ■ more red beads than green beads.

$$4x - 3x = \overbrace{x + \underbrace{x + x + x}_{3x}}^{4x}$$

$$= x$$

19. (a) Simplify $5r - 2r$.

   $5r - 2r = 3r$

There are $r$ beads in each bag.

(b) Simplify $5r - 2r + 3r$.

   $5r - 2r + 3r = 3r + 3r$

   $\qquad\qquad\quad = \blacksquare$

(c) Simplify $5r - 2r + 3$.

   $5r - 2r + 3 = \blacksquare$

(d) Simplify $5r + 3 - 2r + 3r$.

   $5r + 3 - 2r + 3r = \blacksquare$

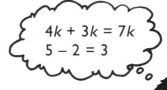

20. Simplify $4k + 5 + 3k - 2$.

   $4k + 5 + 3k - 2 = 7k + 3$

$4k + 3k = 7k$
$5 - 2 = 3$

21. Simplify.
   (a) $5a + 4a$
   (b) $8c - 5c$
   (c) $7k - 2k + k$
   (d) $3x + 6 - x$
   (e) $7m + 7 - 2m$
   (f) $5s + 10 + 2s$
   (g) $2y + 5 + 3y - 2$
   (h) $9 + 4m - 3m - 8$
   (i) $8r + 6 - 2r - 6$
   (j) $8p - 3p - p + 2$
   (k) $8 + 8w + 5 - 2w$
   (l) $7h + h - 4h - h$

Workbook Exercise 3

# PRACTICE 1A

1. Find the value of each of the following expressions when $y = 4$.
   - (a) $21 - y$
   - (b) $y + 25$
   - (c) $3y + 2$
   - (d) $3y$
   - (e) $\dfrac{y}{2}$
   - (f) $\dfrac{y}{16}$
   - (g) $\dfrac{2y - 5}{4}$
   - (h) $y^2 + 4$
   - (i) $2y^2$
   - (j) $y^3 - 20$
   - (k) $\dfrac{3y}{2}$
   - (l) $50 - 3y^2$

Simplify the following expressions.

| | (a) | (b) | (c) |
|---|---|---|---|
| 2. | $x + x + x$ | $3x + 4x$ | $6p - 4p$ |
| 3. | $2p + 2p - p$ | $4r - 2r + 3r$ | $5f - f - 3f$ |
| 4. | $3c - 3c + c$ | $5k + 7 - k$ | $6n + 3 + n + 2$ |
| 5. | $7g - 2g + 2$ | $10x + 5 - 4x - 2$ | $3h + 8 - 3h + 2$ |

6. The admission fee to a bird park is $y. The admission fee to an amusement park is $1 more.
   - (a) Express the admission fee to the amusement park in terms of $y$.
   - (b) If the admission fee to the bird park is $8, find the admission fee to the amusement park.

7. A rope is $x$ m long. An iron rod is 3 times as long as the rope.
   - (a) Express the length of the iron rod in terms of $x$.
   - (b) If the rope is 9 m long, how long is the iron rod?

8. Henry is $x$ years old. Betty is 3 times as old as Henry. Peter is 4 years older than Betty.
   - (a) Express Peter's age in terms of $x$.
   - (b) If Henry is 4 years old, how old is Peter?

9. Huili bought some cartons of milk at $2 each. She gave the cashier $50 and received $y change.
   - (a) Express the number of cartons of milk Huili bought in terms of $y$.
   - (b) If $y = 38$, how many cartons of milk did Huili buy?

# 2 Solid Figures

## ① Drawing Solid Figures

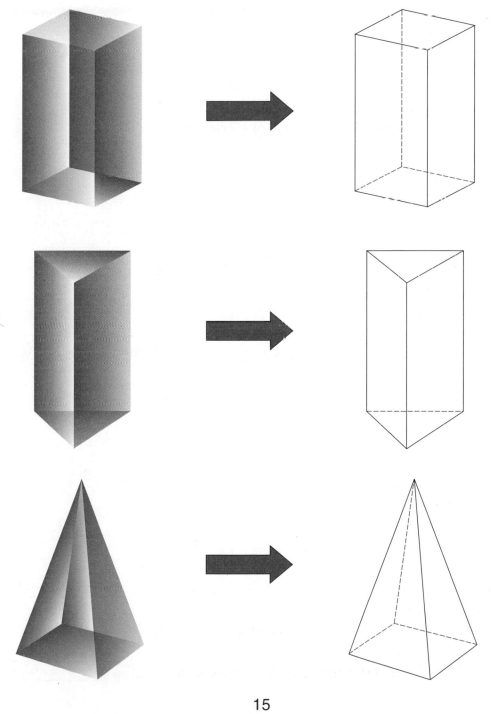

1. The figures below show some solids.
   Which one of the solids has a curved surface?

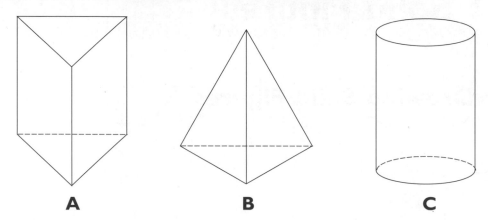

   **A**          **B**          **C**

2. The figures below show some solids.
   How many faces does each solid have?
   How many faces of each solid are triangles?

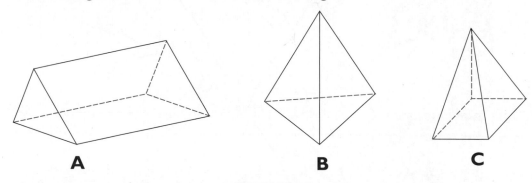

   **A**          **B**          **C**

3. The figures below show some solids.
   Which one of the solids is different from the others? Explain why.

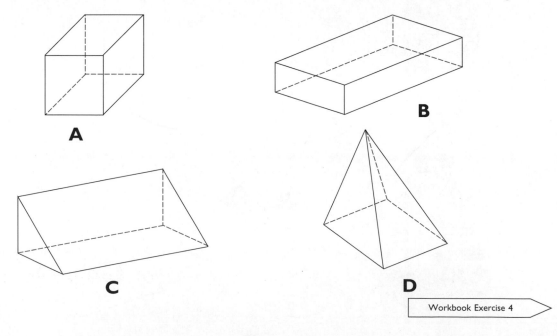

Workbook Exercise 4

16

## 2  Nets

Trace and cut out the figure. Fold it along the lines. You will get a cuboid.

The figure is a **net** of the cuboid.

> A figure which can be folded to form a solid is called a **net** of the solid.

1. Trace and cut out the figures below.
   Fold each figure along the lines to form a solid.

   (a)

   (b)

Workbook Exercise 5

2. This figure shows a solid.

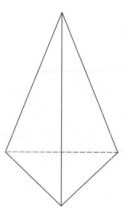

Which of the following can be a net of the solid?

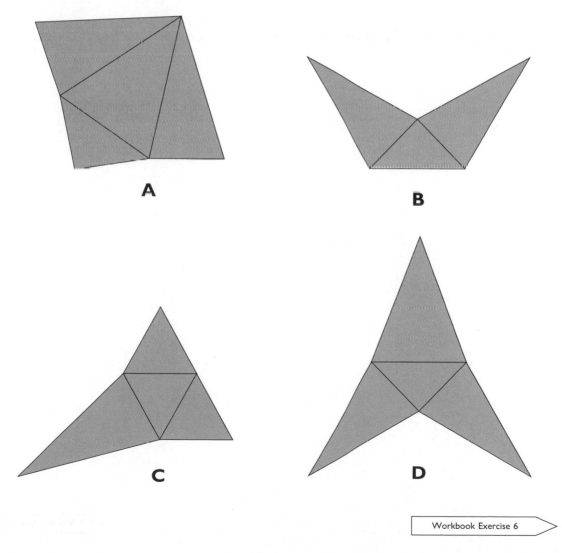

A

B

C

D

Workbook Exercise 6

3. This is a net of a solid.

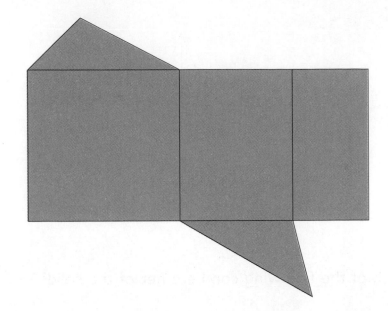

Which one of the following solids can be formed by the net?

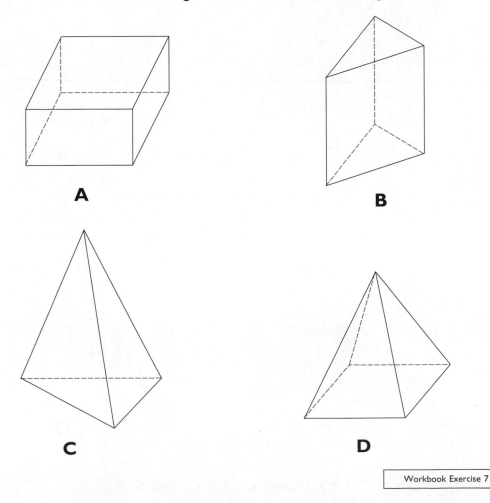

A

B

C

D

Workbook Exercise 7

# 3 Ratio

## 1 Ratio and Fraction

Susan and Mary bought a present which cost $50. Susan, being the elder sister, paid a bigger share of the cost.

Susan's share        Mary's share

We can also show how Susan and Mary shared the cost like this:

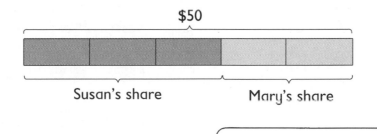

Susan's share        Mary's share

> Susan and Mary shared the cost unequally. Susan's share is 3 units. Mary's share is 2 units. Each unit is $10.

or like this:

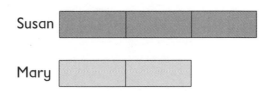

The ratio of Susan's share to Mary's share is 3 : 2.

The ratio of Mary's share to Susan's share is ■ : ■.

1.

(a)  The ratio of the number of bananas to the number of apples is 3 : 4.

(b)  The ratio of the number of oranges to the number of bananas is ■ : ■ .

(c)  The ratio of the number of bananas to the number of apples to the number of oranges is 3 : 4 : 5.

(d)  The ratio of the number of apples to the number of bananas to the number of oranges is ■ : ■ : ■ .

2.

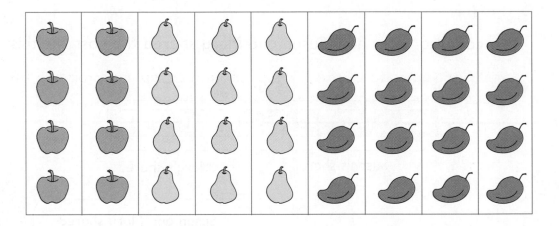

(a)  The ratio of the number of pears to the number of mangoes is 3 : 4.

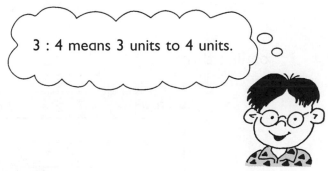

3 : 4 means 3 units to 4 units.

(b)  The ratio of the number of apples to the number of pears to the number of mangoes is ■ : ■ : ■ .

3. There are 35 red beads and 45 green beads.
   (a) Find the ratio of the number of red beads to the number of green beads.

   $$35 : 45 = \blacksquare : \blacksquare$$

   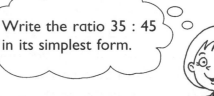

   Write the ratio 35 : 45 in its simplest form.

   (b) Find the ratio of the number of red beads to the number of green beads to the total number of beads.

   $$35 : 45 : 80 = \blacksquare : \blacksquare : \blacksquare$$

   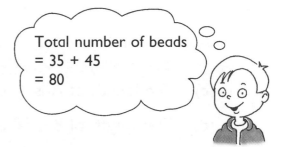

   Total number of beads
   = 35 + 45
   = 80

4. David had $240. He spent $40 on food, $120 on books and saved the rest. Find the ratio of the amount of money spent on food to the amount spent on books to the amount saved.

   $$40 : 120 : 80 = \blacksquare : \blacksquare : \blacksquare$$

   Savings = $240 − $40 − $120
   = $80

5. A rectangle measures 60 cm by 40 cm. Find the ratio of the length to the width to the perimeter of the rectangle.

   $$60 : 40 : 200 = \blacksquare : \blacksquare : \blacksquare$$

   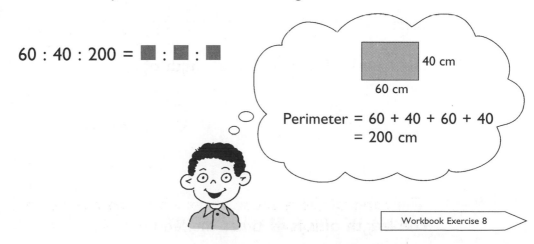

   40 cm
   60 cm

   Perimeter = 60 + 40 + 60 + 40
   = 200 cm

   Workbook Exercise 8

6.

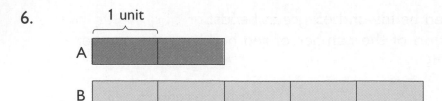

(a) The ratio of the length of A to the length of B is 2 : 5.

(b) The ratio of the length of A to the total length of A and B is 2 : 7.

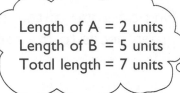

Length of A = 2 units
Length of B = 5 units
Total length = 7 units

(c) The length of A is $\frac{2}{7}$ of the total length.

(d) The length of B is ■ of the total length.

(e)

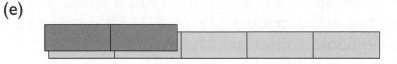

The length of A is $\frac{2}{5}$ of the length of B.

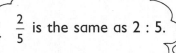

$\frac{2}{5}$ is the same as 2 : 5.

(f)

The length of B is $\frac{5}{2}$ of the length of A.

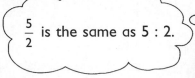

$\frac{5}{2}$ is the same as 5 : 2.

The length of B is ■ times the length of A.

24

7.   The ratio of the number of boys to the number of girls in a class is 4 : 5.

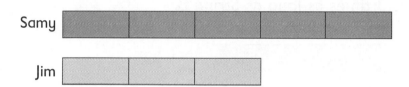

Boys

Girls

(a)   Express the number of boys as a fraction of the number of girls.
(b)   Express the number of girls as a fraction of the number of boys.

8.   The ratio of Samy's money to Jim's money is 5 : 3. Express Samy's money as a fraction of Jim's money.

Samy

Jim

9.   Meihua saved $420 and Sumin saved $350.
(a)   Find the ratio of Meihua's savings to Sumin's savings.

$$\frac{420}{350} = \frac{6}{5}$$

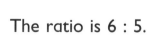

Write the ratio 420 : 350 as a fraction.
Then write the fraction in its simplest form.

The ratio is 6 : 5.

(b)   What is the ratio of Sumin's savings to Meihua's savings?
(c)   What fraction of Sumin's savings is Meihua's savings?

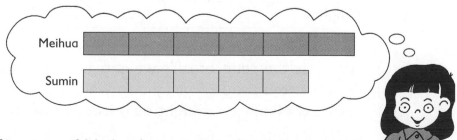

Meihua

Sumin

(d)   What fraction of Meihua's savings is Sumin's savings?

10. A sum of money is shared between Peter, John and Henry in the ratio 2 : 3 : 5.

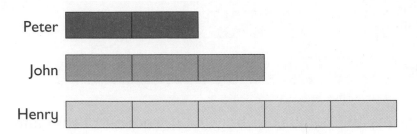

(a) Express Henry's share as a fraction of John's share.
(b) What fraction of the whole sum of money is John's share?


11. String A is 3 times as long as String B.

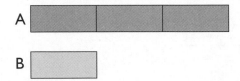

(a) What is the ratio of the length of String A to the length of String B?
(b) What is the ratio of the length of String B to the length of String A?
(c) What fraction of the length of String A is the length of String B?


12. Ali's weight is $\frac{3}{4}$ of Minghua's weight.

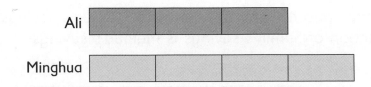

(a) What is the ratio of Ali's weight to Minghua's weight?
(b) What is the ratio of Minghua's weight to Ali's weight?
(c) Express Minghua's weight as a fraction of Ali's weight.

Workbook Exercise 9

13. John, Tom and David share a sum of money in the ratio 4 : 5 : 6. If David receives $60 more than John, find the sum of money shared by the three boys.

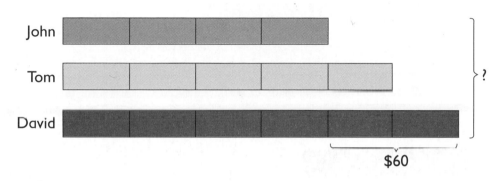

2 units = $60

15 units = $

David's share is 2 units more than John's share.
The total is 15 units.

14. The number of boys is $\frac{3}{5}$ of the number of girls. If there are 120 children altogether, how many boys are there?

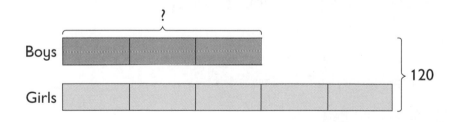

8 units = 120

3 units = ■

Workbook Exercise 10

15. The ratio of the number of Jim's marbles to Raju's is 2 : 1 and the ratio of the number of Raju's marbles to Lihua's is 4 : 5. Find the ratio of the number of Jim's marbles to Raju's to Lihua's.

Jim's : Raju's = 2 : 1

Raju's : Lihua's = 4 : 5

Jim's : Raju's : Lihua's = ■ : ■ : ■

16. $\frac{4}{5}$ of Peter's money is twice as much as Weimin's money. What fraction of Peter's money is Weimin's money?

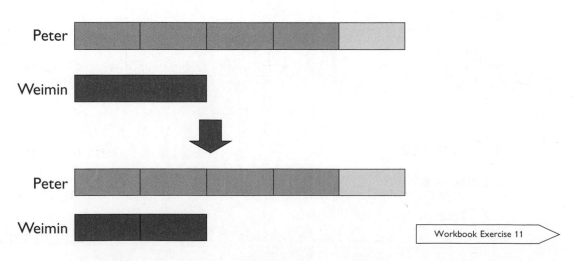

Workbook Exercise 11

# PRACTICE 3A

1. 78 children attended a concert. 60 of them were boys.
   (a) Find the ratio of the number of boys to the number of girls.
   (b) Express the number of boys as a fraction of the number of girls.

2. The weights of Package A and Package B are in ratio 3 : 4.
   (a) Express the weight of Package A as a fraction of Package B.
   (b) Express the weight of Package B as a fraction of Package A.

3. A sum of money was shared among Mary, Nancy and Ann in the ratio 4 : 5 : 6.
   (a) Express Mary's share as a fraction of Ann's share.
   (b) What fraction of the sum of money did Nancy get?

4. Betty's height is $\frac{2}{3}$ of Jinlan's height. Find the ratio of Betty's height to Jinlan's height.

5. The number of Minghua's stamps is $1\frac{1}{2}$ times that of John's. Find the ratio of the number of Minghua's stamps to John's.

6. There are 3 times as many girls as boys in a school choir.
   (a) What is the ratio of the number of girls to the total number of children?
   (b) What fraction of the children are boys?
   (c) If there are 27 girls, how many children are there altogether?

7. The number of men is $\frac{5}{8}$ of the number of women working in a factory. If there are 24 more women than men, how many workers are there altogether?

8. The ratio of the number of men to the number of women in a bus is 3 : 1. The ratio of the number of women to the number of children is 3 : 5.
   (a) Find the ratio of the number of men to the number of women to the number of children.
   (b) If there are 20 children, how many people are there altogether?

# Ratio and Proportion

John used the following table to help him make a mixture of sand and cement.

| Number of buckets of cement | 5 | 10 | 20 | 25 |
|---|---|---|---|---|
| Number of buckets of sand | 3 | 6 | 12 | 15 |

$$\frac{5}{3} = \frac{10}{6} = \frac{20}{12} = \frac{25}{15}$$

The amount of cement and sand used are **in proportion**.

Using the same proportion, how many buckets of cement are needed to mix with 30 buckets of sand?

$$\frac{5}{3} = \frac{}{30}$$

Using the same proportion, how many buckets of sand are needed to mix with 30 buckets of cement?

$$\frac{5}{3} = \frac{30}{}$$

Cement and sand are mixed in the ratio 5 : 3.

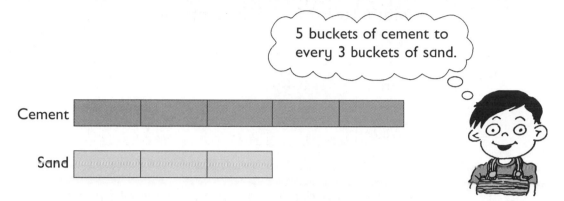

5 buckets of cement to every 3 buckets of sand.

Cement

Sand

1.  To make jello, we mix 2 cups of water with every cup of jello crystals.

Jello crystals                    Water

(a)  Complete the following table.

| Number of cups of jello crystals | 1 | 2 | ■ | 16 |
|---|---|---|---|---|
| Number of cups of water | 2 | 4 | 16 | ■ |

(b)  What is the ratio of the number of cups of jello crystals to the number of cups of water?

2.  Wendy mixed 1 liter of juice concentrate with every 3 liters of water to make a drink for a party.

(a)  Find the ratio of the amount of juice concentrate to the amount of water.

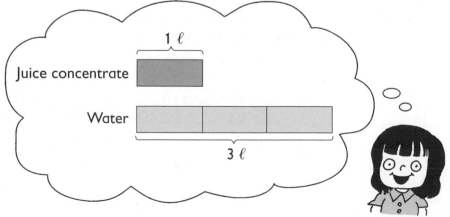

1 ℓ

Juice concentrate

Water

3 ℓ

(b)  To make the same drink, how many liters of water are needed to mix with 6 liters of juice concentrate?

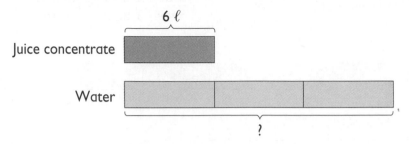

(c)  To make the same drink, how many liters of juice concentrate are needed to mix with 15 liters of water?

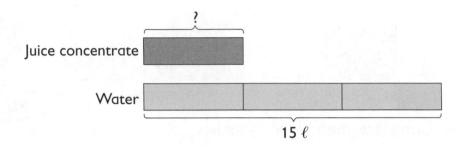

3.  Mr. Ray mixed red paint and blue paint in the ratio 3 : 2 for a painting job.

(a)  If he used 12 liters of red paint, how many liters of blue paint did he use?

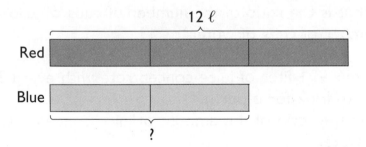

(b)  If he made 10 liters of paint for the painting job, how many liters of red paint did he use?

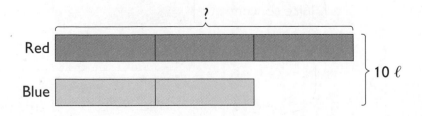

Workbook Exercise 12

32

# PRACTICE 3B

1. To make cookies, Emily mixes 50 g of flour with every 20 g of sugar.
   (a) What is the ratio of the weight of sugar to the weight of flour?
   (b) How many grams of flour are needed to mix with 80 g of sugar?

2. In a school, there are 4 boy scouts to every 3 girl scouts.
   (a) What is the ratio of the number of boy scouts to the number of girl scouts?
   (b) If there are 42 girl scouts, how many boy scouts are there?

3. To make biscuits, Lindsey uses 5 cups of flour to 1 cup of milk.
   (a) If she uses 3 cups of milk, how many cups of flour will she use?
   (b) If she uses 20 cups of flour, how many cups of milk will she use?

4. To make green paint, a painter mixed yellow paint and blue paint in the ratio 3 : 2. If he used 12 gal of yellow paint, how much blue paint did he use?

5. Mary mixed syrup, milk and water in the ratio 2 : 3 : 9 to make a drink. She used 6 cups of syrup. How many cups of drink did she make?

6. A sum of money was shared between Susan and Nancy in the ratio 2 : 5. Nancy received $36 more than Susan. How much money did Susan receive?

7. The ratio of Peter's money to Paul's money is 5 : 3. If Peter has $25, how much money do they have altogether?

8. The ratio of the number of Chinese books to the number of English books in a library is 4 : 7. There are 2200 Chinese books and English books altogether. How many English books are there?

9. The sides of a triangle are in the ratio 4 : 5 : 6. If the perimeter of the triangle is 60 cm, find the length of the shortest side.

# ③ Changing Ratios

The ratio of the number of Peter's stamps to the number of Henry's stamps was 2 : 3. The ratio became 5 : 6 when Peter bought another 8 stamps.

**Before:**

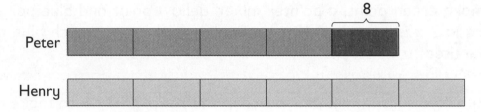

Peter

Henry

**After:**

8

Peter

Henry

The number of my stamps does not change.

Henry

How many stamps did I have at first? How many stamps do I have now?

Peter

1. The ratio of the number of Joe's stamps to Damon's is 2 : 7. Damon has 56 stamps. If Damon gives 8 stamps to Joe, what will be the new ratio of the number of Joe's stamps to Damon's?

**Before:**

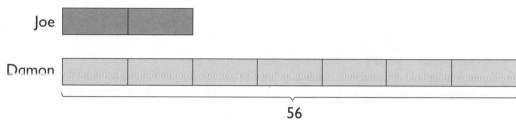

Joe

Damon

56

7 units = 56
1 unit  = 56 ÷ 7 = 8
Number of Joe's stamps = 2 units = 8 × 2 = 16

**After:**
Number of Joe's stamps = 16 + 8 = 24
Number of Damon's stamps = 56 − 8 = 48
New ratio = 24 : 48 = ■ : ■

2. The ratio of the number of Matthew's books to Susan's is 2 : 3. Matthew has 40 books. If Matthew buys another 8 books, what will be the new ratio of the number of Matthew's books to Susan's?

**Before:**

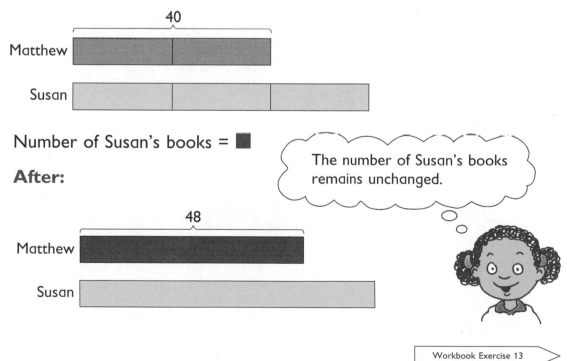

40

Matthew

Susan

Number of Susan's books = ■

**After:**

48

Matthew

Susan

The number of Susan's books remains unchanged.

Workbook Exercise 13

3.  The ratio of the number of marbles in Box A to that in Box B is 4 : 3. If $\frac{1}{2}$ of the marbles in Box A are moved to Box B, what will be the new ratio of the number of marbles in Box A to that in Box B?

**Before:**

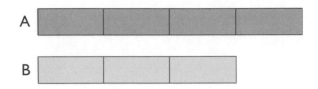

**After:**

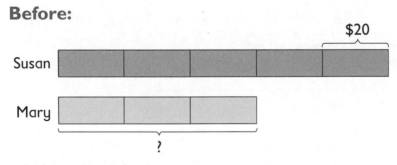

4.  The ratio of Susan's money to Mary's money was 5 : 3 at first. After Susan gave $20 to Mary, they had an equal amount of money each. How much money did Mary have at first?

**Before:**

**After:**

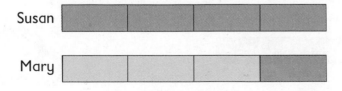

1 unit  = $20

3 units = $▇

5. The ratio of Ian's money to Juan's money is 2 : 3. After spending $\frac{1}{2}$ of his money, Juan has $60 less than Ian. How much money does Ian have?

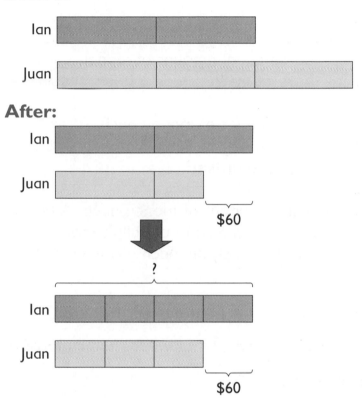

**Before:**

Ian

Juan

**After:**

Ian

Juan

$60

?

Ian

Juan

$60

6. John and Matthew had an equal amount of money each. After John spent $25 and Matthew spent $18, the ratio of John's money to Matthew's money was 2 : 3. How much money did each boy have at first?

**Before:**

?

John

Matthew

**After:**

John

$25

Matthew

$18

Workbook Exercise 14

37

# PRACTICE 3C

1. The ratio of boys to girls in a school choir is 4 : 3. There are 6 more boys than girls. If another 2 girls join the choir, what will be the new ratio of boys to girls?

2. The ratio of Peter's money to Henry's money was 5 : 3 at first. After Peter spent $12, they had an equal amount of money each. How much money did Peter have at first?

3. Ali and Samy had an equal amount of money each. After Samy gave $15 to Ali, the ratio of Ali's money to Samy's money was 7 : 5. How much money did each boy have at first?

4. Sally and Susan had an equal amount of money each. After Sally spent $15 and Susan spent $24, the ratio of Sally's money to Susan's money was 4 : 3. How much money did each girl have at first?

5. The number of Jim's stamps is $\frac{3}{4}$ of the number of David's stamps. If Jim gives $\frac{1}{2}$ of his stamps to David, what will be the ratio of the number of Jim's stamps to David's?

6. The ratio of the number of Meili's books to Sulin's was 1 : 2 at first. After Meili bought another 12 books, the ratio became 2 : 1.
   (a) How many books did Sulin have?
   (b) If Sulin now buys another 5 books, what will be the new ratio of the number of Meili's books to Sulin's?

7. The ratio of the number of marbles in Box A to that in Box B is 3 : 7. Box B has 12 more marbles than Box A.
   (a) How many marbles are there altogether?
   (b) If 3 marbles are moved from Box A to Box B, what will be the new ratio of the marbles in Box A to that in Box B?

8. The ratio of John's money to Sumin's money was 5 : 2 at first. After John spent $\frac{1}{2}$ of his money, he had $20 more than Sumin.
   (a) How much money did Sumin have?
   (b) How much money did John have at first?

# REVIEW A

1. Write the following in figures.
   (a) Forty thousand, five hundred eighty
   (b) Two million, seventy thousand

2. Write the following in words.
   (a) 600,230                    (b) 8,005,000

3. The population of a town is 109,028. Round off the number to the nearest hundred.

4. A condo is sold for about $210,000. Which one of the following could be the actual selling price of the condo?
   $195,000,     $204,000,     $214,000,     $218,000

5. What is the missing number in each ∎?
   (a) 16,045 = 16,000 + ∎
   (b) 42.036 = 42 + $\dfrac{36}{∎}$

6. Find the value of each of the following:
   (a) 12 − 4 ÷ 2 + 6            (b) 24 + 6 × 7 ÷ 3
   (c) (4 + 8) × 3 ÷ 4           (d) 25 − (6 + 9 × 2) + 5

7. Write down a common factor of 32, 64 and 76.

8. Which one of the following is a multiple of 8?
   4,     12,     18,     24

9. (a) Write $\dfrac{7}{8}$ as a decimal.
   (b) Express $4\dfrac{2}{3}$ as a decimal correct to 2 decimal places.

10. (a) Express 0.006 as a fraction in its simplest form.
    (b) Express 1.8 as a mixed number in its simplest form.

11. What is the missing number in each ∎?
    (a) 3 : 6 = ∎ : 18                    (b) 14 : 21 = 2 : ∎
    (c) 20 : 8 : 4 = ∎ : ∎ : 2            (d) $\dfrac{2}{3}$ = ∎ : 3

12. Mrs. King used 2 bags of flour to make 15 cup cakes. How many cup cakes can she make with 10 bags of flour?

13. Find the value of each of the following when $x = 6$.
    (a) $26 + x$          (b) $32 - x$          (c) $7x$

    (d) $\dfrac{8x}{3}$          (e) $3x + 7$          (f) $2x^2$

14. Simplify each of the following expressions.
    (a) $14y - 5y + y$          (b) $10y + 15 - 3y - 8$

15. Kristi bought 2 big boxes and 1 small box of oranges. There were 60 oranges in each big box and 48 oranges in the small box. Find the average number of oranges in each box.

16. The total weight of 3 men is 164.4 kg. If the average weight of 2 of them is 54.9 kg, what is the weight of the third man?

17. Mr. Nelson bought 200 T-shirts. He donated 20 T-shirts to charity and sold the rest at $5 each. Overall, he still earned $360. Find the cost price of one T-shirt.

18. At a fruit stand, oranges are sold at 5 for $2. Peter wants to buy 100 oranges for a party. He has only $35.50. How much more money does he need?

19. $\dfrac{1}{4}$ of a cake weighs $\dfrac{1}{2}$ kg. What is the weight of $\dfrac{1}{2}$ of the cake in kilograms?

20. A container is filled with $\dfrac{1}{2}$ liter of water. If $\dfrac{3}{8}$ of the water is poured out, how much water is left in the container? Give your answer in liters.

21. Sally made some cookies. She sold $\dfrac{3}{4}$ of them and had 20 cookies left. How many cookies did she make?

22. A tank is $\dfrac{3}{5}$ filled with water. When 500 ml of water is poured out, the tank becomes $\dfrac{1}{2}$ full. Find the capacity of the tank in liters.

23. Jim spent $\dfrac{1}{5}$ of his money on books and $\dfrac{3}{8}$ of the remainder on a cassette recorder. He had $250 left.
    (a) What fraction of his money did he have left?
    (b) How much money did he have at first?

24. $\frac{1}{4}$ of the roses in a garden are red, $\frac{1}{3}$ of the remainder are yellow and the rest are pink. There are 24 more pink roses than red roses. How many roses are there altogether?

25. The ratio of Jim's weight to Eva's weight is 5 : 4. Express Jim's weight as a fraction of Eva's weight.

26. Meili's savings is $\frac{1}{3}$ of Sumin's savings.

    (a) What is the ratio of Sumin's savings to Meili's savings?
    (b) If Sumin saves $20 more than Meili, how much does Meili save?

27. The ratio of the number of swordtails to the number of angelfish in a fish tank is 2 : 3. The number of swordtails is $\frac{1}{4}$ of the number of guppies.

    (a) Find the ratio of the number of swordtails to the number of angelfish to the number of guppies.
    (b) If there are 25 more guppies than angelfish, how many fish are there altogether?

28. John, Peter and Henry shared a sum of money in the ratio 6 : 3 : 5. Henry received $80 more than Peter. How much money did John receive?

29. The ratio of Aziz's money to Osman's money was 2 : 1 at first. After Aziz spent $10, the ratio became 4 : 3. How much money did each boy have at first?

30. John can type 80 words per minute.
    (a) How many words can he type in 10 minutes?
    (b) How long will he take to type a passage which contains 2000 words?

31. Mary bought 600 g of raisins at $0.45 per 100 g. How much did she pay?

32. The rates of advertising in a newspaper are as follows:

| First 10 words | $9 |
|---|---|
| Every additional word | $0.60 |

What is the cost of an advertisement which has 16 words?

33. How many faces does the solid have?

34. Which of the following are nets of a cube?

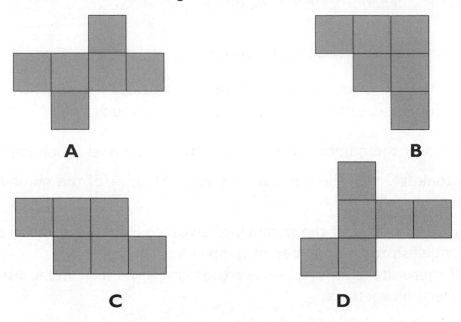

**A**

**B**

**C**

**D**

35. The figure is made up of 3 rectangles of the same size. Find its perimeter.

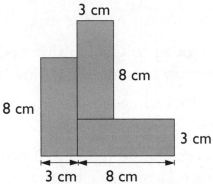

3 cm

8 cm

8 cm

3 cm

3 cm   8 cm

36. The figure is made up of a square and a triangle. Find its area.

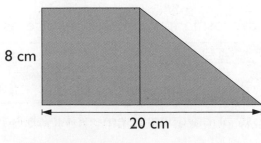

8 cm

20 cm

# REVIEW B

1. What fraction of each figure is shaded?
   (a) 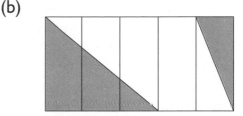 (b)

2. Write $6 \div 5$ as a mixed number.

3. What is the missing number in each ■?

   (a) $3\frac{1}{3} = \frac{■}{3}$
   
   (b) $\frac{7}{5} = 1 + \frac{■}{5}$

4. What is the missing number in each ■?
   (a) $7540 = 7000 + ■ + 40$      (b) $1038 = ■ + 38$
   (c) $3.49 = 3 + ■$              (d) $0.624 = 0.6 + ■$

5. The factors of 12 are 1, 2, 3, 4, ■ and 12. What is the missing number in the ■?

6. (a) Write down a common multiple of 3, 4 and 9.

   (b) Find the value of $\frac{1}{3} + \frac{1}{4} + \frac{1}{9}$.

7. Which one of the following decimals is the greatest?
   0.83,     0.4,     0.097,     0.265

8. Which one of the following fractions is the smallest?
   $\frac{3}{5}$,     $\frac{5}{6}$,     $\frac{2}{3}$,     $\frac{3}{4}$

9. (a) Express $1\frac{2}{5}$ ℓ in milliliters.

   (b) Express $1\frac{1}{4}$ m in centimeters.

10. (a) Express 1.72 km in meters.
    (b) Express 125 minutes in hours and minutes.

11. Eric took 5 hours and 40 minutes to drive from Los Angeles to San Francisco. He left Los Angeles at 10:30 a.m. What time did he arrive in San Francisco?

12. Find the value of each of the following:
    (a)  300,000 + 28,000          (b)  102,000 − 97,000
    (c)  8000 × 30                 (d)  96,000 ÷ 600

13. Which one of the following is the best estimate of the amount of water in the container?
    1.5 ℓ,     1.7 ℓ,     1.9 ℓ

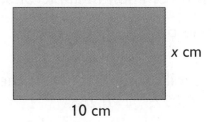

14. The scale shows the weight of a boy.

    Which one of the following is the best estimate of the weight of the boy?
    47 kg,     47.5 kg,     47.9 kg

15. Ashley is 12 years old. Her mother is *m* years older than she.
    (a)  How old will her mother be in 5 years' time? Give the answer in terms of *m*.
    (b)  If $m = 20$, how old will her mother be in 5 years' time?

16.

*x* cm

10 cm

    (a)  Express the perimeter of the rectangle in terms of *x*.
    (b)  If $x = 6$, find the perimeter of the rectangle.

17. In a class of 38 students, 4 boys and 2 girls are absent. What fraction of the students are present?

18. Joe has $35. Connor has $10 less than Joe. Connor has twice as much money as Tyler. How much money do they have altogether?

19. Melissa paid a total of $15.50 for 3 kg of cherries and 5 mangoes. At the same shop, Emily paid $8.80 for 4 mangoes. Find the price of 1 kg of cherries.

20. The average weight of 4 sacks of carrots is 18 kg. If 3 sacks weigh 17.5 kg each, what is the weight of the fourth sack?

21. Mrs. Lee bought 1 kg of flour. She used $\frac{1}{4}$ of it to make cakes and $\frac{1}{5}$ of the remainder to make biscuits. How many grams of flour did she use altogether?

22. Mrs. Oswald made some cookies. $\frac{1}{3}$ of them were butter cookies, $\frac{2}{5}$ were cherry cookies and the rest were chocolate cookies. There were 30 more cherry cookies than butter cookies. How many chocolate cookies were there?

23. John spent $\frac{1}{3}$ of his money on a plate of noodles and a glass of drink. He still had $9 left. If the plate of noodles cost $3.60, find the cost of the glass of drink.

24. Lauren read 42 pages of a book on Monday. She read $\frac{2}{5}$ of the book on Tuesday. If she still had $\frac{1}{4}$ of the book to read, how many pages were there in the book?

25. Ryan and Juan had $500 altogether. After Ryan spent $80, he had $\frac{3}{5}$ as much money as Juan.
    (a) How much money did Juan have?
    (b) How much money did Ryan have at first?

26. Mr. Bode mixed 3 cups of flour with every cup of milk to make pancakes. If he used a total of 24 cups of flour and milk, how many cups of milk did he use?

27. Taylor had 72 chicken pies, 54 fruit pies and 36 beef pies. Find the ratio of the number of beef pies to the number of chicken pies to the number of fruit pies.

28. Miranda cuts a raffia 84 in. long into two pieces in the ratio 5 : 9. What is the length of the longer piece?

29. Angela, Betty and Carol shared a sum of money in the ratio 4 : 2 : 5.
    (a) What fraction of the sum of money did Carol receive?
    (b) If Carol received $15 more than Betty, how much money did Angela receive?

30. The ratio of the number of men to the number of women in a parade is 5 : 3. The ratio of the number of children to the number of adults is 1 : 2. Find the ratio of the number of men to the number of women to the number of children.

31. Ali's money is $\frac{3}{5}$ of David's money.

   (a) What is the ratio of Ali's money to David's money?

   (b) If David gives $\frac{1}{2}$ of his money to Ali, what will be the new ratio of Ali's money to David's money?

32. Find the area of the shaded triangle.

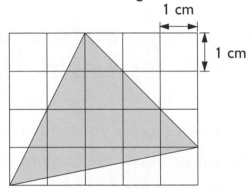

33. The figure is made up of a rectangle and a triangle. Find its area and perimeter.

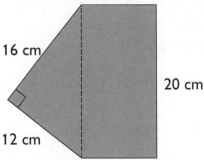

34. The rectangles P and Q are equal in area. If the perimeter of P is 32 cm, find the perimeter of Q.

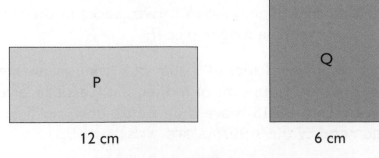

46

# 4 Percentage

## 1 Part of a Whole as a Percentage

The table shows the enrollment in a music school.

| | |
|---|---|
| Number of boys | 240 |
| Number of girls | 360 |
| Total number | 600 |

What percentage of the students are boys?

> Write 240 out of 600 as $\frac{240}{600}$ and then express it as a percentage.

**Method 1:**

$$\frac{240}{600} = \frac{40}{100}$$
$$= 40\%$$

**Method 2:**

$$\frac{240}{600} \times 100\% = 40\%$$

What percentage of the students are girls?

1. Express each of the following as a percentage.
   (a) 13 out of 50

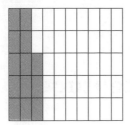

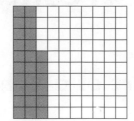

Write 13 out of 50 as $\frac{13}{50}$ and then express it as a percentage.

$\frac{13}{50} = $  %

   (b) 120 out of 300

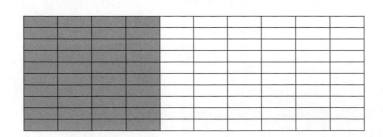

$\frac{120}{300} = $ ■ %

2. Express each of the following as a percentage.
   (a) 6 out of 100     (b) 2 out of 10     (c) 3 out of 50
   (d) 4 out of 25     (e) 18 out of 200     (f) 75 out of 300

3. Express each fraction as a percentage.

(a) $\dfrac{24}{50}$

(b) $\dfrac{16}{25}$

(c) $\dfrac{30}{75}$

(d) $\dfrac{180}{600}$

(e) $\dfrac{60}{150}$

(f) $\dfrac{15}{250}$

4. Express $\dfrac{3}{5}$ as a percentage.

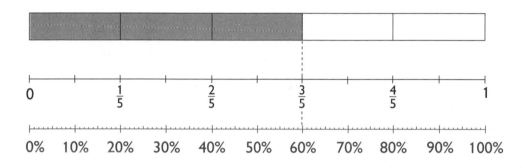

$$\dfrac{3}{5} \times 100\% = 60\%$$

1 whole is 100%.

$\dfrac{3}{5}$ is 60%.

5. Express $\dfrac{1}{8}$ as a percentage.

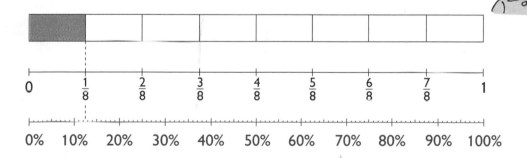

$$\dfrac{1}{8} \times 100\% = \blacksquare\%$$

1 whole is 100%.

$\dfrac{1}{8}$ is $\blacksquare$%.

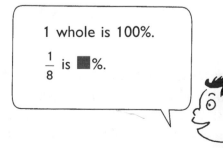

6. Express each fraction as a percentage.

   (a) $\dfrac{1}{4}$          (b) $\dfrac{1}{5}$          (c) $\dfrac{3}{4}$

   (d) $\dfrac{4}{5}$          (e) $\dfrac{3}{8}$          (f) $\dfrac{7}{10}$

Workbook Exercise 15

7. Express each percentage as a fraction in its simplest form.
   (a) 5%          (b) 8%          (c) 50%
   (d) 15%         (e) 44%        (f) 78%

8. Express 0.8 as a percentage.

   $0.8 \times 100\% = \blacksquare \%$

9. Express 0.075 as a percentage.

   $0.075 \times 100\% = \blacksquare \%$

10. Express each decimal as a percentage.
   (a) 0.1       (b) 0.9       (c) 0.01       (d) 0.03
   (e) 0.75      (f) 0.001      (g) 0.045     (h) 0.225

11. Express each percentage as a decimal.
   (a) 3%          (b) 35%        (c) 40%        (d) 86%

Workbook Exercise 16

12.  28 out of 40 students in a class walk to school. The rest go to school by bus.

(a) What percentage of the students walk to school?

$$\frac{28}{40} \times 100\% = 70\%$$

(b) What percentage of the students go to school by bus?

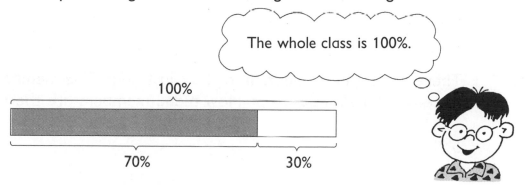

The whole class is 100%.

100%

70%   30%

13.  Ali had $120. He spent 40% of the money on a watch and 25% of the remainder on a pen.

(a) What percentage of his money did he spend?

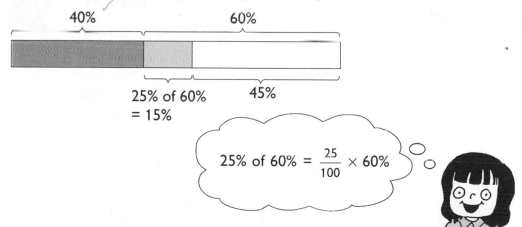

40%          60%

25% of 60%        45%
= 15%

$$25\% \text{ of } 60\% = \frac{25}{100} \times 60\%$$

(b) How much money did he have left?

45% of $120

Workbook Exercises 17 & 18

14. A bookshop gives a 20% discount during a sale. Thomas bought a dictionary and a storybook which cost $40 and $15 respectively. How much did he have to pay altogether?

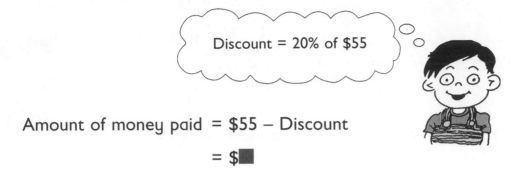

Discount = 20% of $55

Amount of money paid = $55 – Discount

$$= \$\blacksquare$$

15. There were 140 members in a choir last year. The membership was increased by 15% this year. How many members are there this year?

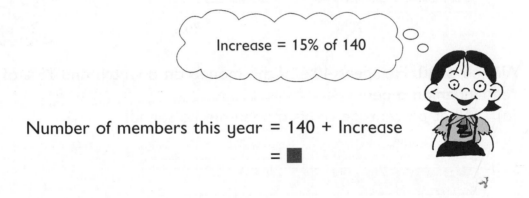

Increase = 15% of 140

Number of members this year = 140 + Increase

$$= \blacksquare$$

16. Elliot bought a bicycle which cost $600. In addition, he had to pay 3% sales tax. How much did he pay for the bicycle?

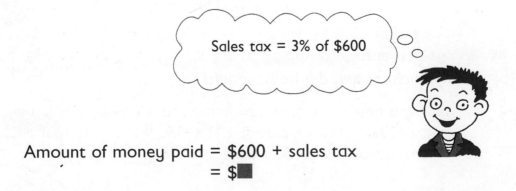

Sales tax = 3% of $600

Amount of money paid = $600 + sales tax

$$= \$\blacksquare$$

Workbook Exercise 19

# PRACTICE 4A

1. Express each of the following as a fraction in its simplest form.
   (a) 8%         (b) 25%        (c) 50%        (d) 66%

2. Express each of the following as a decimal.
   (a) 9%         (b) 90%        (c) 15%        (d) 62%

3. Express each of the following as a percentage.
   (a) $\dfrac{2}{5}$    (b) $\dfrac{7}{8}$    (c) $\dfrac{9}{20}$    (d) $\dfrac{30}{600}$
   (e) 0.5        (f) 0.08       (g) 0.15       (h) 0.245

4. Jen spends 85% of her pocket money and saves the rest. What percentage of her pocket money does she save?

5. 45% of a pole is painted red, 20% is painted blue and the rest is painted white. What percentage of the pole is painted white?

6. 36 out of 400 seats in a cinema are vacant. What percentage of the seats are vacant?

7. $\dfrac{2}{5}$ of the students in a school wear glasses. What percentage of the students in the school wear glasses?

8. Eva had 3 m of cloth. She used 75 cm of it to make a dress for her doll. What percentage of the cloth did she use for the dress?

9. 45 medals were given out at a band competition. There were 22 bronze medals and 14 silver medals. The rest were gold medals. What percentage of the medals were gold medals?

10. Kristin spends 30% of her savings on a watch and 60% of the remainder on a dress. What percentage of her savings is left?

# PRACTICE 4B

1.  Find the value of each of the following.
    (a)  9% of 125
    (b)  78% of 900
    (c)  30% of $250
    (d)  45% of 400 m
    (e)  21% of 50 ℓ
    (f)  16% of 60 kg

2.  Henry deposited $1500 in a bank. The bank paid 4% interest per year. How much money did he receive as interest after 1 year?

3.  Nicholas shot 15 arrows. 40% of the arrows hit the target. How many arrows did not hit the target?

4.  There are 125 rooms in a building. 64% of them are air-conditioned. How many rooms are not air-conditioned?

5.  The usual price of a compact disc player was $200. At a sale, it was sold at a discount of 5%. What was the selling price?

6.  Cody's monthly salary was increased by 5% this year. His monthly salary before the increase was $1400. Find his monthly salary after the increase.

7.  Liping has 300 stamps. 60% of them are U.S. stamps, 24% are Canadian stamps and the rest are European stamps. How many European stamps does she have?

8.  Marilyn bought 1.6 kg of ground meat. She used 350 g of it to make meatballs and 80% of the remainder to make hamburgers. How many grams of ground meat did she have left?

9.  Rachel went to the market with $80. She spent 15% of the money on vegetables and 50% of the remainder on meat. How much did she spend on meat?

10. In a class of 40 students, 60% are girls. 50% of the girls and 25% of the boys wear glasses. How many students wear glasses?

## ② One Quantity as a Percentage of Another

Sumin saves $400 and Meihua saves $500.
Express Meihua's savings as a percentage of Sumin's savings.

> Take Sumin's savings as 100%.
> Meihua's savings is ■%.

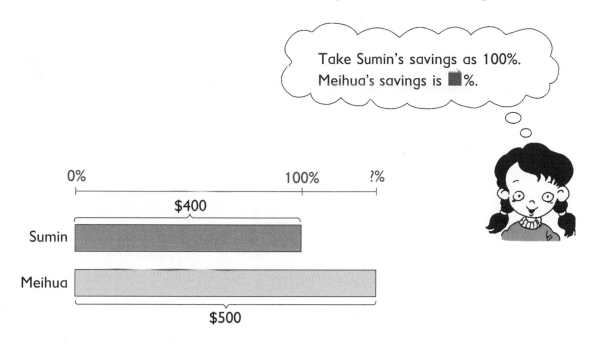

$400 $\longrightarrow$ 100%

$1 $\longrightarrow$ $\frac{100}{400}$%

$500 $\longrightarrow$ $\frac{100}{400} \times 500$%

$= 125$%

Meihua's savings is 125% of Sumin's savings.

> Meihua saves $100 more than Sumin.
>
> Meihua saves 25% more than Sumin.

Express Sumin's savings as a percentage of Meihua's savings.

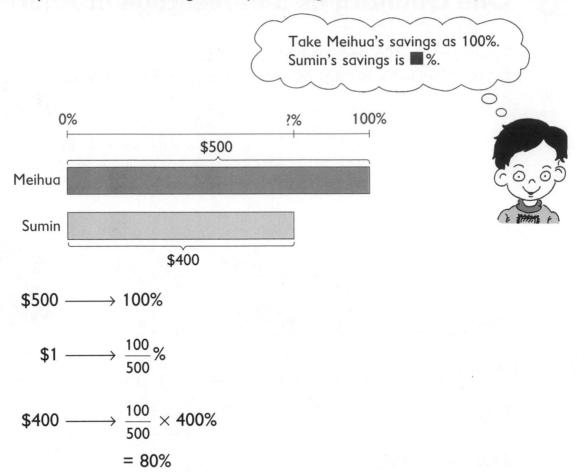

Take Meihua's savings as 100%. Sumin's savings is ▇%.

$500 ⟶ 100%

$1 ⟶ $\frac{100}{500}$ %

$400 ⟶ $\frac{100}{500} \times 400$%

= 80%

Sumin's savings is 80% of Meihua's savings.

Sumin saves $100 less than Meihua.

Sumin saves 20% less than Meihua.

Meihua saves 25% more than Sumin but Sumin saves 20% less than Meihua.

1. What percentage of $3 is 30¢?

$$\frac{30}{300} \times 100\% = \blacksquare\%$$

$3 = 300¢

30¢ is $\blacksquare$% of $3.

2. Express 300 ml as a percentage of 2 ℓ.

$$\frac{300}{2000} \times 100\% = \blacksquare\%$$

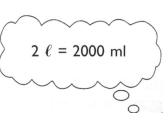

2 ℓ = 2000 ml

300 ml is $\blacksquare$% of 2 ℓ.

3. Express 1.35 m as a percentage of 90 cm.

$$\frac{135}{90} \times 100\% = \blacksquare\%$$

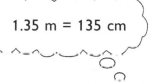

1.35 m = 135 cm

1.35 m is $\blacksquare$% of 90 cm.

Workbook Exercise 20

4. The cost price of a television set is $1200. It is sold for $900. Express the selling price as a percentage of the cost price.

$$\frac{900}{1200} \times 100\% = \blacksquare\%$$

The selling price is $\blacksquare$% of the cost price.

5. The usual price of a vacuum cleaner is $150. It is sold for $120.
   (a) How much is the discount?

   Discount = $150 − $120

   = $30

   (b) Express the discount as a percentage of the usual price.

   $$\frac{30}{150} \times 100\% = \blacksquare\%$$

   The discount is ■% of the usual price.

6. Shimin weighed 40 kg last year. She weighs 43 kg now. Express the increase in weight as a percentage of her weight last year.

   Increase in weight = 43 − 40

   = 3 kg

   $$\frac{3}{40} \times 100\% = \blacksquare\%$$

   The increase is ■% of her weight last year.

Workbook Exercise 21

7. There are 50 men and 40 women at a party. How many percent more men than women are there?

   Express the difference in number as a percentage of the number of women.

   Difference in number = 50 − 40 = ■

   Percentage = ■%

58

8. Ian has $56. Brandon has 20% more money than Ian. How much money does Brandon have?

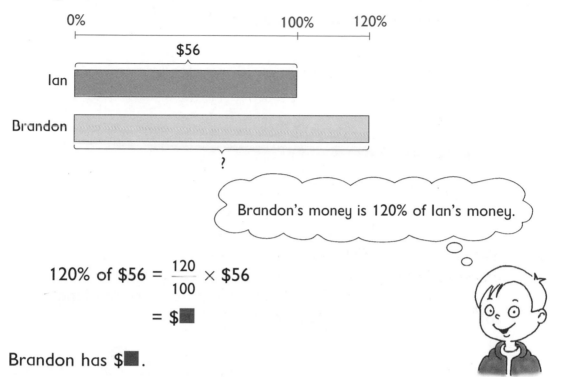

Brandon's money is 120% of Ian's money.

$$120\% \text{ of } \$56 = \frac{120}{100} \times \$56$$

$$= \$\blacksquare$$

Brandon has $\blacksquare$.

9. Package A weighs 5 kg. Package B weighs 15% less than Package A. Find the weight of Package B.

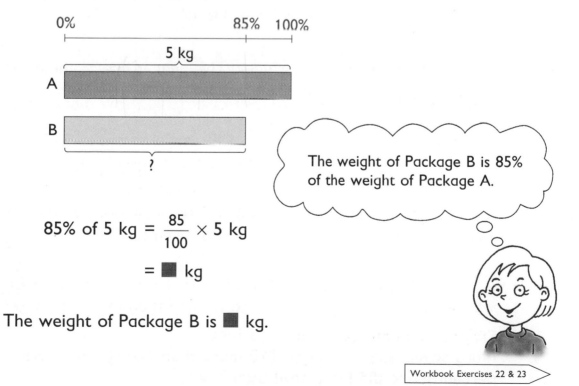

The weight of Package B is 85% of the weight of Package A.

$$85\% \text{ of } 5 \text{ kg} = \frac{85}{100} \times 5 \text{ kg}$$

$$= \blacksquare \text{ kg}$$

The weight of Package B is $\blacksquare$ kg.

Workbook Exercises 22 & 23

# PRACTICE 4C

1.      Express 480 ml as a percentage of 1.5 ℓ.

2.      What percentage of 2 hours is 30 minutes?

3.

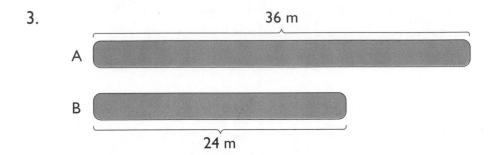

     (a)   Express the length of A as a percentage of the length of B.
     (b)   How many percent longer is A than B?

4.      Mrs. Brooks had 2.5 kg of sugar. She used 650 g of it to make syrup.
        What percentage of the sugar was used for making the syrup?

5.      The price of a television set was reduced from $200 to $150. By
        what percentage was the price reduced?

6.      A club had 80 members last year. This year it has 96 members. By
        what percentage was the membership increased?

7.      The price of beef increased from $12 per kilogram to $15 per
        kilogram. Express the increase as a percentage of the original price.

8.      Kyle bought a pair of shoes for $51. The usual price of the shoes was
        $60. How many percent discount was given to Kyle?

9.      A factory has 600 workers. 250 of them are men and the rest are
        women. How many percent more women than men are there?

10.     Mary saved $35. She saved $10 more than Nancy. How many
        percent more did Mary save than Nancy?

# 3 Solving Percentage Problems by Unitary Method

Sean sells a set of furniture for $3600. The selling price is 20% more than the cost price. Find the cost price of the set of furniture.

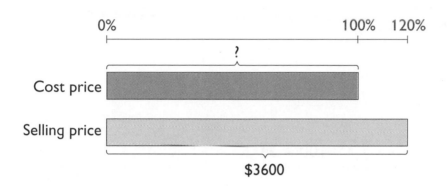

The selling price is 120% of the cost price.

120% $\longrightarrow$ $3600

1% $\longrightarrow$ $\dfrac{3600}{120}$

100% $\longrightarrow$ $\dfrac{3600}{120} \times 100$

$= \$\blacksquare$

The cost price of the set of furniture is $\blacksquare$.

1. Meili scored 42 points in a test. This was 75% of the total score. Find the total score.

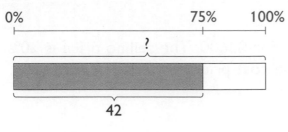

75% $\longrightarrow$ 42

1% $\longrightarrow$ $\dfrac{42}{75}$

100% $\longrightarrow$ $\dfrac{42}{75} \times 100 =$ ■

The total score was ■.

2. Jim's salary is $864. This is 90% of Adam's salary. Find Adam's salary.

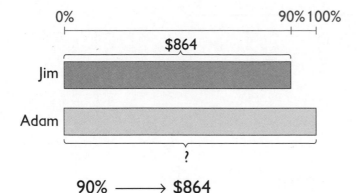

90% $\longrightarrow$ $864

1% $\longrightarrow$ $$\dfrac{864}{90}$

100% $\longrightarrow$ $$\dfrac{864}{90} \times 100 =$ $■

Adam's salary is $■.

Workbook Exercise 24

3.  During a sale, the price of a blouse was reduced by 15%. It was sold for $17. Find the usual price of the blouse.

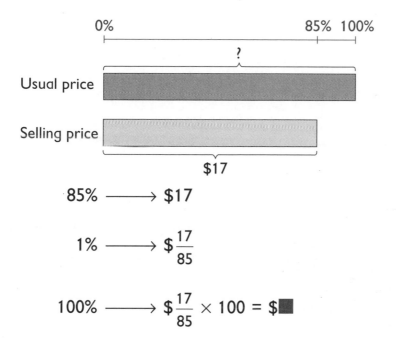

$$85\% \longrightarrow \$17$$

$$1\% \longrightarrow \$\frac{17}{85}$$

$$100\% \longrightarrow \$\frac{17}{85} \times 100 = \$\blacksquare$$

The usual price of the blouse was $\blacksquare$.

4.  The number of books in Rahman's library was increased by 20% to 180. Find the number of books before the increase.

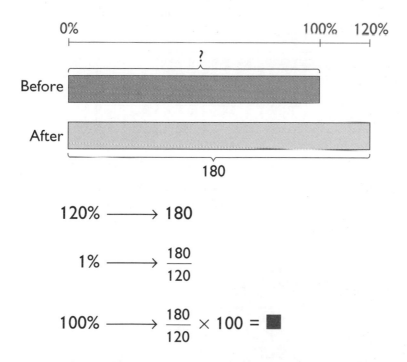

$$120\% \longrightarrow 180$$

$$1\% \longrightarrow \frac{180}{120}$$

$$100\% \longrightarrow \frac{180}{120} \times 100 = \blacksquare$$

There were $\blacksquare$ books in the library before the increase.

5. Kelly's monthly salary is increased by 10%. The increase is $120. Find her monthly salary after the increase.

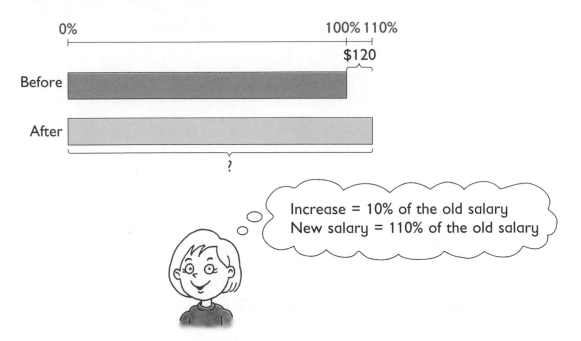

Before

After

?

Increase = 10% of the old salary
New salary = 110% of the old salary

6. If a salesman sells a watch at 80% of the cost price, the watch will be sold at $600. At what price must he sell the watch if he wants to make $150?

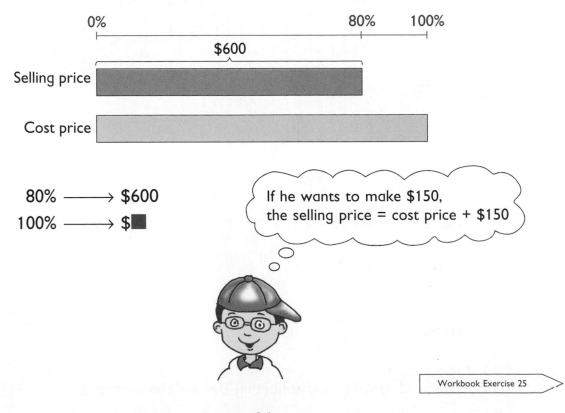

Selling price

Cost price

$600

80% ⟶ $600
100% ⟶ $■

If he wants to make $150,
the selling price = cost price + $150

Workbook Exercise 25

7. James saved $44 in June. He saved 10% more in June than in May. How much did he save in May?

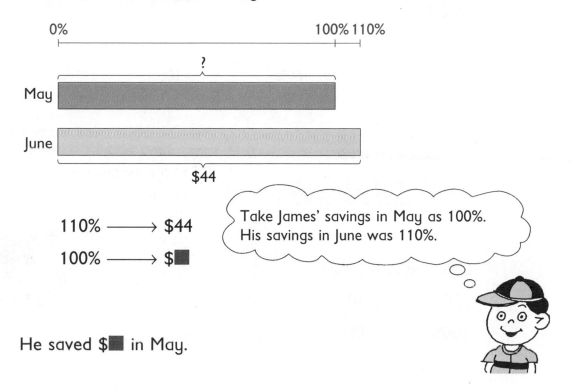

110% ⟶ $44
100% ⟶ $▮

Take James' savings in May as 100%. His savings in June was 110%.

He saved $▮ in May.

8. Mary has 180 books. She has 10% fewer books than John. How many books does John have?

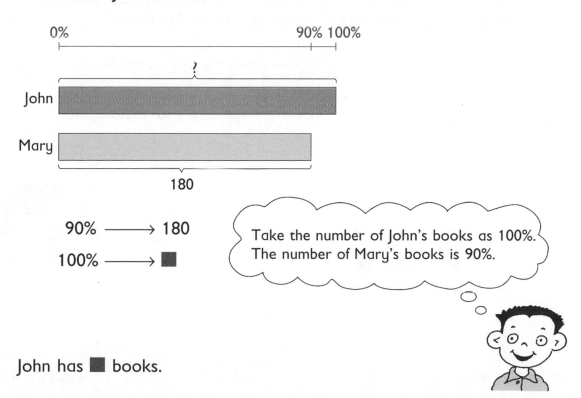

90% ⟶ 180
100% ⟶ ▮

Take the number of John's books as 100%. The number of Mary's books is 90%.

John has ▮ books.

9. In a school, 40% of the teachers are males. There are 18 more female teachers than male teachers. How many teachers are there altogether?

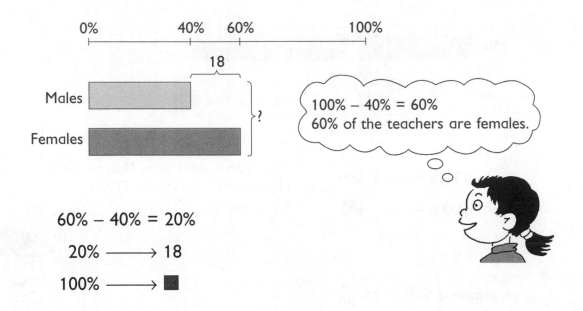

$$60\% - 40\% = 20\%$$
$$20\% \longrightarrow 18$$
$$100\% \longrightarrow \blacksquare$$

10. At a parking lot, 80% of the spaces are for cars, 8% are for buses and the rest are for motorcycles. If there are 24 spaces for motorcycles, how many spaces are there for buses?

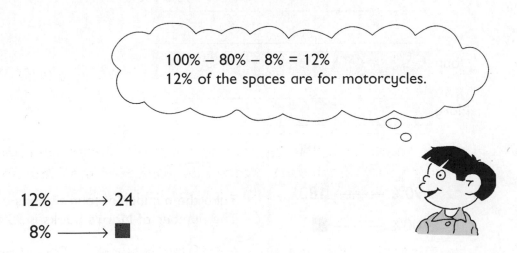

$$12\% \longrightarrow 24$$
$$8\% \longrightarrow \blacksquare$$

Workbook Exercise 26

# PRACTICE 4D

1. Madison saves $240 every month. This is 20% of her monthly salary. What is her monthly salary?

2. 12% of the entries for an art competition won prizes. If 132 entries won prizes, find the total number of entries.

3. In a quiz, Trevor answered all the questions. He answered 90% of the questions correctly and 5 questions incorrectly. How many questions did he answer correctly?

4. 60% of the books in a library are for adults, 5% are for young people and the rest are for children. If there are 280 books for children, how many books are there altogether?

5. At a sale, Jenny bought a fan for $140. This was 70% of its usual price. What was the usual price of the fan?

6. Mary bought a dress at a discount of 25%. If the discount was $15, find the usual price of the dress.

7. Juan sold a bicycle at a discount of 15%. If the selling price was $340, find the usual price of the bicycle.

8. Emily's score for a Mathematics test was 5% higher than her score for an English test. If Emily scored 84 points for the Mathematics test, how many points did she score for the English test?

9. Jake spent $55 this week. He spent 10% more this week than last week. How much did he spend last week?

10. There are 10% more boys than girls in a choir. If there are 4 more boys than girls, how many children are there altogether?

# PRACTICE 4E

1. Mrs. Coles had 1.5 kg of flour. She used 600 g to bake a cake. What percentage of the flour was used for baking the cake?

2. 60% of the students in a class are boys. If there are 16 girls in the class, how many boys are there?

3. Andy's pay is 20% less than his supervisor's pay. If Andy's pay is $1500, what is his supervisor's pay?

4. A tire is sold at a discount of 10%. It is sold for $45. Find the usual price of the tire.

5. In a test, there were 50 questions. Tim answered 80% of them correctly. Carlos answered 90% of them correctly.
   (a) How many more questions did Carlos answer correctly than Tim?
   (b) How many percent more questions did Carlos answer correctly than Tim?

6. There are 200 members in a club. 60% of them are males. How many percent more males than females are there?

7. 40% of the beads in a box are red and the rest are yellow. There are 36 more yellow beads than red beads. How many beads are there altogether?

8. A shop gave different discounts to different customers. Libby paid $600 for a watch at a discount of 20%. However, Scott paid $630 for the same watch. How many percent discount was given to Scott?

9. Mary's salary is 10% more than Alice's. If their total salary is $4200, what is Mary's salary?

10. John spent 20% of his money on food. He spent $\frac{2}{5}$ of the remainder on a toy. The toy cost $12.
    (a) What percentage of his money did he spend on the toy?
    (b) How much money did he have at first?

# REVIEW C

1. Write each fraction in its simplest form.

   (a) $\dfrac{36}{48}$

   (b) $\dfrac{350}{500}$

2. What number must be added to $2\dfrac{4}{5}$ to make 3?

3. Find the missing number in each ■.

   (a) $\dfrac{11}{8} = 1 + \blacksquare$

   (b) $4 - \blacksquare = 3\dfrac{1}{8}$

   (c) $\dfrac{7}{10} = \blacksquare \times \dfrac{1}{10}$

   (d) $\dfrac{8}{9} = 4 \times \dfrac{\blacksquare}{9}$

4. 5 girls share 3 pizzas equally. What fraction of a whole pizza will each girl receive?

5. John had $\dfrac{1}{2}$ of a pancake. He cut it into 6 equal pieces. What fraction of a whole pancake was one piece?

6. Express each fraction as a decimal.

   (a) $\dfrac{7}{20}$

   (b) $2\dfrac{1}{5}$

7. Write each decimal as a fraction In Its simplest form.
   (a) 0.075

   (b) 1.04

8. Which one of the following is the same as 0.6?
   $\dfrac{1}{2}$, $\quad$ $\dfrac{2}{3}$, $\quad$ $\dfrac{3}{4}$, $\quad$ $\dfrac{3}{5}$

9. Which one of the following is nearest to 7?
   6.7, $\quad$ 6.96, $\quad$ 7.08, $\quad$ 7.5

10. (a) What fraction of 2 hours is 20 minutes?
    (b) What fraction of 2 liters is 500 ml?

11. Find the value of each of the following:
    (a) $5 \times (13 - 9) + 8 \div 4$
    (b) $8 \times (52 - 47) \div 2$

12. Which one of the following is 18 km correct to the nearest kilometer?
    18.54 km, $\quad$ 17.93 km, $\quad$ 18.81 km, $\quad$ 17.25 km

13. Express $\frac{8}{9}$ as a decimal correct to 2 decimal places.

14. (a) Round off 54,826 to the nearest thousand.
    (b) Round off 4.09 to the nearest whole number.
    (c) Round off 4.073 to 1 decimal place.

15. Express $\frac{5}{8}$ as a percentage.

16. Express 0.235 as a percentage.

17. Express each of the following as a fraction in its simplest form.
    (a) 80%                                    (b) 5%

18. Express each of the following as a decimal.
    (a) 6%                                     (b) 92%

19. Find the value of each of the following:
    (a) 5% of 30 kg                            (b) 60% of 350 m

20. Express 2.5 kg as a percentage of 10 kg.

21. $\frac{2}{5}$ of a number is 42. What is $\frac{1}{3}$ of the number?

22. The average of 45, 56, ■ and 75 is 60. Find the missing number in the ■.

23. A wheel makes 650 revolutions in $\frac{1}{2}$ hour. At this rate, how many revolutions will it make in 3 hours?

24. 5 oranges cost $1.90. Find the cost of 15 oranges.

25. 5 cans of drinks cost $3. How many cans of drinks can I buy with $15?

26. 3 towels cost $2.40. Emily bought 6 such towels and gave the cashier $10. How much change did she receive?

27. There are 200 more green balls than red balls in a box. When another 50 red balls are put in the box, there are twice as many green balls as red balls. How many green balls are there in the box?

70

28. 3 boys collected 75 kg of newspaper. Another 2 boys collected 30 kg of newspaper. Find the average weight of newspaper collected by each boy.

29. Alex sold 160 oranges and 90 apples. He sold the oranges at 5 for $1.20 and the apples at 3 for $1. How much money did he receive?

30. $\frac{1}{4}$ of Jim's savings is $350. How much is Jim's savings?

31. Justin spends $\frac{3}{5}$ of his money on 15 mangoes and 9 pears. If 1 mango costs twice as much as 1 pear, how many pears can he buy with the rest of his money?

32. Mr. Davis had 18 kg of grapes. He sold $\frac{2}{3}$ of them at $5.25 per kilogram and the remainder at $4.80 per kilogram. How much money did he receive altogether?

33. A bottle contains 420 ml of water when it is $\frac{3}{5}$ full. What is the capacity of the bottle?

34. $\frac{2}{5}$ of the marbles in a box are yellow, $\frac{1}{3}$ of the remainder are blue and the rest are red. If there are 10 more red marbles than blue marbles, how many marbles are there altogether?

35. Janet bought $\frac{1}{2}$ a cake. She ate $\frac{1}{4}$ of the cake she bought. Then she cut the remainder into 2 equal pieces. What fraction of a whole cake was each piece?

36. A tank is $\frac{2}{5}$ filled with water. When another 26 liters of water are poured in, the tank becomes $\frac{5}{6}$ full. Find the capacity of the tank.

37. There are 24 balloons in a packet. 6 of them are blue, 10 of them are green and the rest are red. Find the ratio of the number of blue balloons to the number of green balloons to the number of red balloons.

38. In a basket, there are apples, oranges and pears. The ratio of the number of apples to the number of oranges is 1 : 3. The ratio of the number of apples to the number of pears is 2 : 9. Express the number of pears as a fraction of the total number of fruits in the basket.

39. The usual price of a handbag is $60. It is sold at a discount of 15%. Find the discount.

40. 15% of the members in a school choir are girls. If there are 18 girls, how many boys are there?

41. 480 people visited the Science Center. 65% of them were children. How many more children than adults were there?

42. Henry bought a book at a discount of 20%. The discount was 90 cents. How much did he pay for the book?

43. A shop sold 1600 liters of paint last week. This week it sold 2000 liters of paint. By how many percent was the sales increased?

44. The food stalls at a carnival collected 20% more money than the games stalls. If the food stalls collected $1500, how much did the games stalls collect?

45. Linda has some postcards. 20% of them are local postcards and the rest are foreign postcards. If 20% of the foreign postcards are from England, what percentage of the total number of postcards are from England?

46. The figure is made up of a rectangle and a square. Find the shaded area in the figure.

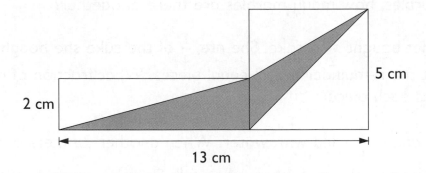

47. Find the shaded area in the square.

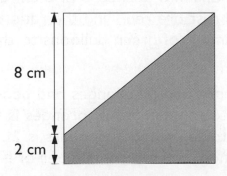

72

48. Which one of the following can be a net of a cuboid?

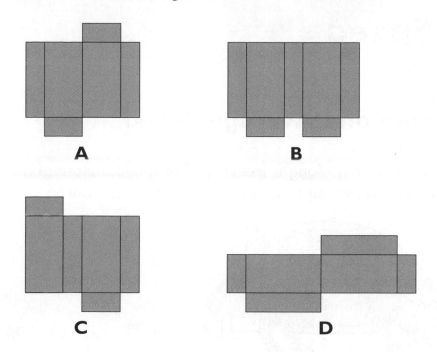

**A**

**B**

**C**

**D**

49. A school has five 6th grade classes. There are **40** students in each class. The bar graph shows the number of students who wear glasses in each class.

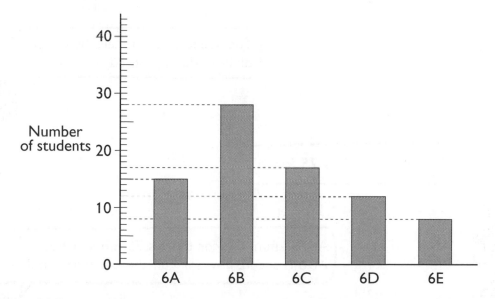

(a) What is the average number of students who wear glasses in each class?

(b) What percentage of the total number of students in the 6th grade wear glasses?

(c) What percentage of the students in 6B do not wear glasses?

# 5 Speed

## 1 Speed and Average Speed

Jacob is driving along a freeway. The speedometer of his car shows that he is traveling at a **speed** of 75 km per hour.

75 km/h

The speed of a car tells how fast or how slowly the car is traveling.

We write 75 km per hour as **75 km/h**.

At 75 km/h, the car travels 75 km in 1 hour.
At this speed, how far can the car travel in 3 hours?

In 1 hour, the car travels 75 km.

In 2 hours, it travels 150 km.

In 3 hours, it travels ■ km.

1. Read the speed shown by each speedometer.

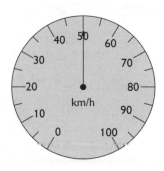 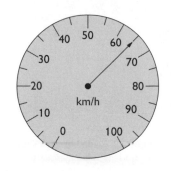 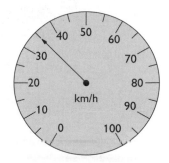

 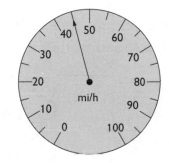 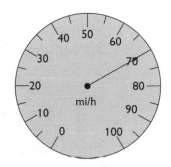

2. A van is traveling at a speed of 50 mi/h. How far can it travel in 2 hours?

$50 \times 2 = $ ■

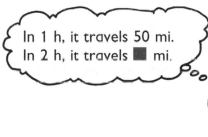

In 1 h, it travels 50 mi.
In 2 h, it travels ■ mi.

It can travel ■ mi in 2 h.

3. Eric is swimming at a speed of 40 m/min. How far can he swim in 5 minutes?

$40 \times 5 = $ ■

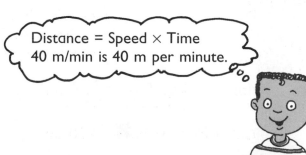

Distance = Speed × Time
40 m/min is 40 m per minute.

He can swim ■ m in 5 min.

4.  A bullet travels 420 m in 2 seconds. Find its speed in m/s.

2 s ⟶ 420 m
1 s ⟶ ? m

420 ÷ 2 = ▨

Its speed is ▨ m/s.

5.  Ravi is running at a certain speed. He runs a distance of 150 m in 30 seconds. Find his speed in m/s.

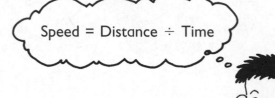

Speed = Distance ÷ Time

150 ÷ 30 = ▨

Ravi's speed is ▨ m/s.

Workbook Exercise 27

6.  A bus traveled 220 km in 4 hours. Find its **average speed** in km/h.

**Average speed** is the average distance traveled per hour.

220 ÷ 4 = ▨

Its average speed was ▨ km/h.

7.  Mary walked 534 m in 6 minutes. Find her average speed in m/min.

534 ÷ 6 = ▨

Her average speed was ▨ m/min.

8. A train traveled 245 km at an average speed of 70 km/h. What was the time taken?

Time taken = $\dfrac{245}{70}$

       = ■ h

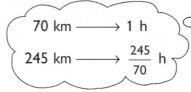

70 km ⟶ 1 h

245 km ⟶ $\dfrac{245}{70}$ h

9. Amber walked 720 m from her house to the market. Her average speed for the trip was 90 m/min. How long did she take to walk from her house to the market?

Time taken = 720 ÷ 90

       = ■ min

Time = Distance ÷ Speed

Workbook Exercise 28

10. John started cycling at 7:30 a.m. By 9:30 a.m. he had covered a distance of 20 mi.

(a) Find his average speed in mi/h.

Average speed = $\dfrac{20}{2}$ = 10 mi/h

The duration from 7:30 a.m. to 9:30 a.m. is 2 h.

(b) If he cycled a further distance of 15 mi at the same average speed, what would be the time then?

Time taken = $\dfrac{15}{10}$ = 1.5 h

1.5 h after 9:30 a.m. is ■ a.m.

11. Colin took 4 hours to drive from Town P to Town Q at an average speed of 75 km/h. On his way back, he drove at an average speed of 60 km/h. How long did he take to drive back from Town Q to Town P?

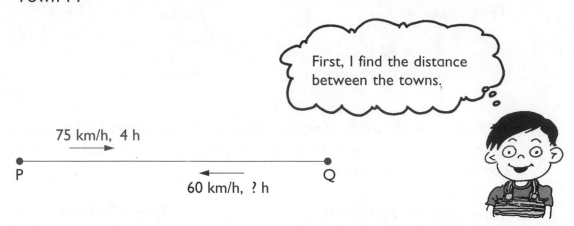

First, I find the distance between the towns.

75 km/h, 4 h

P

60 km/h, ? h

Q

Distance between P and Q = 75 × 4 = 300 km

Time taken for the return trip = $\frac{300}{60}$ = ■ h

12. A motorcyclist took 7 hours to travel from Town X to Town Y at an average speed of 35 km/h. A van took only 5 hours for the same trip. Find the average speed of the van.

35 km/h, 7 h

X

? km/h, 5 h

Y

Distance between X and Y = 35 × 7 = 245 km

Average speed of the van = $\frac{245}{5}$ = ■ km/h

Workbook Exercise 29

13. A motorist traveled on a freeway for 2 hours at 80 km/h. He then traveled for another 3 hours at 70 km/h. Find his average speed for the whole trip.

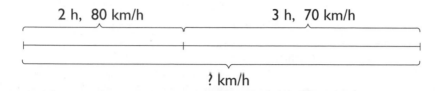

2 h, 80 km/h     3 h, 70 km/h

? km/h

Total distance traveled = ■ km

Total time taken = ■ h

Average speed for the whole trip = ■ km/h

14. Brian drove from Town P to Town Q. He traveled the first 36 km at an average speed of 54 km/h. He traveled the remaining 96 km at an average speed of 72 km/h. Find his average speed for the whole trip.

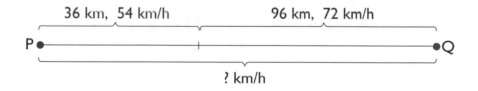

36 km, 54 km/h     96 km, 72 km/h

P●————————————————————●Q

? km/h

Total distance traveled = ■ km

Total time taken = ■ h

Average speed for the whole trip = ■ km/h

Workbook Exercise 30

15. Kevin took 3 hours to cover $\frac{2}{3}$ of a trip. He covered the remaining 120 km in 2 hours. Find his average speed for the whole trip.

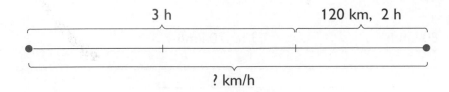

3 h      120 km, 2 h

? km/h

Total distance traveled = ■ km

Total time taken = ■ h

Average speed for the whole trip = ■ km/h

16. A motorist took 4 hours to travel from Town A to Town B. His average speed for the whole trip was 60 km/h. For the first $\frac{4}{5}$ of the trip, he traveled at an average speed of 64 km/h. Find his average speed for the remaining trip.

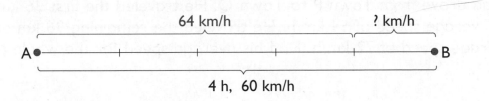

64 km/h      ? km/h

A ●————————————————● B

4 h, 60 km/h

Distance between A and B = 60 × 4 = 240 km

$\frac{1}{5}$ of the trip = ■ km

$\frac{4}{5}$ of the trip = ■ km

Time taken for the first $\frac{4}{5}$ of the trip = ■ h

Time taken for the remaining trip = ■ h

Average speed for the remaining trip = ■ km/h

Workbook Exercise 31

# PRACTICE 5A

1. John is swimming at a certain speed. He swims 50 m in 40 seconds. Find his speed in m/s.

2. A ball rolled 450 cm in 15 seconds. Find its average speed in cm/s.

3. An express train is traveling at a speed of 420 mi/h. How far can it travel in 3 hours?

4. Mitchell is running at a speed of 6 m/s. How long will he take to run a distance of 300 m?

5. A train left Station X at 8:30 a.m. for Station Y. The distance between the two stations was 250 km. At what time would it reach Station Y if its average speed was 100 km/h?

6. Ryan took 15 minutes to walk to school at an average speed of 70 m/min. His brother took 20 minutes to walk the same distance. Find his brother's average speed.

7. Daniel took 2 hours to drive from Town A to Town B at an average speed of 60 km/h. How long would he take if he drove at an average speed of 80 km/h?

8. Cameron took 8 minutes to run round a 400-m track 4 times. Find his average speed in m/min.

9. A car left Town A at 9:30 a.m. and reached Town B at 11:30 a.m. Its average speed was 60 km/h. Find the distance between Town A and Town B.

10. The distance between Marisa's house and the post office is 720 m. If she walks from her house to the post office at an average speed of 80 m/min, how long will she take?

# PRACTICE 5B

1. The diagram shows the route of a bus from Town A to Town D.

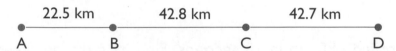

| 22.5 km | 42.8 km | 42.7 km |

A          B          C          D

The bus left Town A at 2:30 p.m. and arrived at Town D at 4:30 p.m. Find its average speed for the whole trip.

2. Danny took 2 hours to cycle from Town A to Town B. His average speed was 10 km/h.
   (a) Find the distance between the two towns.
   (b) If his average speed was increased by 2 km/h, how much time would he take for the trip?

3. Ben and David both cycled a distance of 24 km. They started at the same time. David completed the trip 20 minutes earlier than Ben. If David's average speed was 9 km/h, find Ben's average speed.

4. Paul took 5 minutes to walk from his house to the main road at an average speed of 46 m/min. He then took another 10 minutes to walk to his office at 40 m/min. How far did he walk altogether?

5. A group of boys went on a 12-km hike. For the first 3 km, they walked at an average speed of 4 km/h. For the rest of the hike, they walked at an average speed of 6 km/h. Find the total time taken.

6. Andrew drove from Town X to Town Y. He took 2 hours to travel $\frac{4}{5}$ of the trip. He took 1 hour to travel the remaining 30 km.
   (a) Find the distance between the two towns.
   (b) Find his average speed for the whole trip.

7. A motorist traveled from Town P to Town Q. After traveling $\frac{1}{3}$ of the trip at an average speed of 45 km/h, he continued to travel another 240 km to reach Town Q.
   (a) Find the distance between the two towns.
   (b) If his average speed for the whole trip was 54 km/h, find his average speed for the last $\frac{2}{3}$ of the trip.

# REVIEW D

1.  Write the following in words.
    (a)  30,600
    (b)  2,470,000

2.  What is the missing number in each ■?
    (a)  In 3685, the value of the digit 6 is ■.
    (b)  In 5.327, the value of the digit 7 is ■.

3.  (a)  What number is 1000 more than 25,327?
    (b)  What number is 100 less than 43,569?

4.  What is the missing number in each ■?
    (a)  $2406 = 2000 + ■ + 6$
    (b)  $3.805 = 3 + 0.8 + ■$

5.  Find the value of each of the following:
    (a)  $7600 \div 200$
    (b)  $12.5 \times 16$

6.  (a)  Round off  8.74 to 1 decimal place.
    (b)  Round off  2.395 to 2 decimal places.

7.  Which one of the following numbers has 3 as a factor?
    13,      23,      33,      43

8.  Find the value of each of the following:
    (a)  $24 + 18 \div 3 \times 2$
    (b)  $(12 + 13) \div 3 + 2 \times 4$

9.  What is the missing number in each ■?
    (a)  $1.8 \times ■ = 18$
    (b)  $0.13 \times ■ = 130$
    (c)  $3.4 \div ■ = 0.034$
    (d)  $60.1 \div ■ = 6.01$

10.  How many quarters are there in $1\frac{3}{4}$?

11.  Write each of the following as a decimal.
     (a)  $3 + \dfrac{6}{10} + \dfrac{4}{1000}$
     (b)  $\dfrac{15}{1000} + \dfrac{4}{100}$

12.  Write $3 + \dfrac{5}{12}$ as a decimal correct to 2 decimal places.

13. Which one of the following is the best estimate of the amount of water in the container?

120 ml,    140 ml,    160 ml

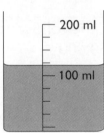

14. Find the value of each of the following:

(a) $1\frac{1}{4}$ kg = ■ g

(b) $1\frac{2}{3}$ h = ■ min

15. What is the missing number in each ■?
(a) 9 : 3 = 3 : ■

(b) 1 : 4 : 3 = 9 : ■ : ■

16. Express each of the following as a percentage.
(a) 15 out of 40

(b) 270 out of 600

17. Express each of the following as a fraction in its simplest form.
(a) 0.084

(b) 28%

18. Express 1.4 m as a percentage of 2 m.

19. Find the value of each of the following:
(a) 15% of 900

(b) 30% of 4800

20. Ray bought a compact disc for $15 and a poster for $3. He had $12 left.
(a) Find the ratio of the amount of money spent on the compact disc to the amount of money spent on the poster to the amount of money left.
(b) What fraction of the total amount of money was spent on the compact disc?
(c) What percentage of the total amount of money was spent on the compact disc?

21. Jamlah's weight is $\frac{4}{3}$ of Devi's weight. What is the ratio of Jamlah's weight to Devi's weight?

22. $\frac{3}{5}$ of John's stamps are Canadian stamps. What percentage of his stamps are Canadian stamps?

23. Peter sold 60 pencils at 5 for $1.20. How much money did he receive?

24. 8 mangoes cost $12. How many mangoes will cost $15?

25. 100 g of bananas cost $0.15. Find the cost of 600 g of bananas.

26. A shop charged $3 for developing a roll of film and 25 cents for printing each picture. How much did Sarah pay for developing a roll of film and printing 35 pictures?

27. Mrs. Hart spent $\frac{3}{5}$ of her money on a bag and $\frac{1}{6}$ on a belt. She had $14 left. How much money did she have at first?

28. $\frac{3}{8}$ of a group of children are girls. There are 20 more boys than girls. How many children are there altogether?

29. Alice read $\frac{1}{4}$ of a book on Sunday. She read 6 more pages on Monday than on Sunday. If she still had 36 pages to read, how many pages did she read on Sunday?

30. The ratio of the number of teachers to the number of students in a school is 2 : 25. How many students are there if there are 8 teachers?

31. The length and width of a rectangle are in the ratio 3 : 2. If the length of the rectangle is 9 cm, find its area.

32. Juan has twice as much money as Tom. They have $240 altogether. If Juan gives $20 to Tom, what will be the new ratio of Juan's money to Tom's money?

33. Kendra had $850. She gave $400 to her parents and spent 40% of the remainder. How much money did she have left?

34. Kirsten spent 40% of her money on a watch which cost $28. How much money did she have at first?

35. Mrs. Holt took 10 minutes to walk to the market at an average speed of 3 km/h. How many meters did she walk?

36. Mr. Glass drove from Town P to Town Q. He traveled a distance of 240 km at an average speed of 80 km/h. If he left Town P at 8:10 a.m., what time did he arrive at Town Q?

37. Russell and Pablo started driving from Town X to Town Y at the same time. At the end of 2 hours, Russell reached Town Y while Pablo completed only $\frac{2}{3}$ of the trip.

   (a) If Russell's average speed for the whole trip was 75 km/h, find Pablo's average speed for the first $\frac{2}{3}$ of the trip.

   (b) If Pablo's average speed for the last $\frac{1}{3}$ of the trip was increased by 10 km/h, how long did he take for the last $\frac{1}{3}$ of the trip?

38. The bar graph shows the number of students in 6 groups. Study the graph and answer the questions which follow.

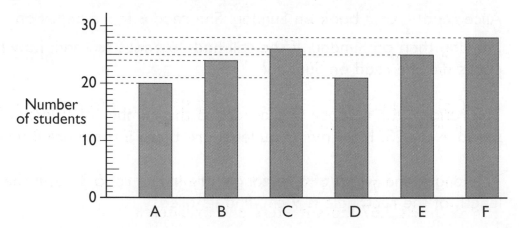

   (a) Which group has more students than Group D but less students than Group E?
   (b) What is the ratio of the number of students in Group B to the number of students in Group F?
   (c) How many percent more students are there in Group C than in Group A?

# REVIEW E

1. What is the missing number in each 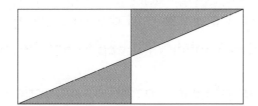?
   (a) The digit 5 in 457,806 stands for $5 \times$ ■.
   (b) The value of the digit 4 in 2.461 is ■.

2. Find the value of each of the following:
   (a) $(59 + 13) \div (4 \times 2)$          (b) $18 \div (6 + 3) \times 2$

3. The distance between Town A and Town B is about 5 km. Which one of the following could be the actual distance?
   4.299 km,     4.387 km,     4.479 km,     4.501 km

4. Divide 348 by 24. Express your answer as a decimal.

5. What fraction of the rectangle is shaded?

6. What is the missing number in each ■?

   (a) $\dfrac{3}{10} + \dfrac{1}{10} + \dfrac{1}{10} = $ ■ $\times \dfrac{1}{10}$        (b) $27.031 = 27 + \dfrac{31}{■}$

7. Mr. Goldberg earns $2400. He saves $400. What fraction of his earnings does he save?

8. (a) Express $1\dfrac{1}{3}$ hours in hours and minutes.

   (b) Express 2.67 liters in liters and milliliters.

9. What is the missing number in each ■?

   (a) $\dfrac{7}{10}$ m = ■ cm             (b) $\dfrac{4}{5}$ kg = ■ g

   (c) $2\dfrac{3}{10}$ ℓ = ■ ml           (d) $1\dfrac{1}{2}$ h = ■ min

10. Express $2\frac{5}{8}$ as a decimal correct to 2 decimal places.

11. Find the average value of 2.74 kg, 1.9 kg and 3.04 kg correct to 1 decimal place.

12. 320 out of 500 families in a city have computers. What percentage of the families have computers?

13. Express $\frac{1}{40}$ as a percentage.

14. 6 pears cost $1.50. How many pears will cost $9?

15. At a supermarket, crab meat was sold at $0.72 per 100 g. Rachel bought 450 g of crab meat from the supermarket. How much did she pay?

16. $\frac{4}{9}$ of the beads in a box are green and the rest are yellow.
    (a) Find the ratio of the number of green beads to the number of yellow beads.
    (b) Express the number of yellow beads as a fraction of the number of green beads.

17. $\frac{2}{3}$ of David's money is equal to $\frac{1}{2}$ of John's money. What is the ratio of David's money to John's money?

18. An egg costs 15 cents. How many eggs will cost $3?

19. 4 cakes of soap weigh 480 g. Find the weight of 3 cakes of soap.

20. If oranges are sold at 3 for $2, how much must I pay for 12 oranges?

21. Anne bought 8 exercise books and a file. She gave the cashier $10 and received $2.05 change. If each exercise book cost 55 cents, how much did the file cost?

22. Jared earned 40 cents from every magazine he sold. He earned an extra $3 for every 30 magazines sold. How many magazines did he sell if he earned $450 altogether?

23. An egg tray with 12 eggs weighs 440 g. The empty tray weighs 20 g. What is the average weight of an egg?

24. From January to August last year, James sold an average of 4.5 cars each month. He did not sell any car in the next 4 months.
    (a) On the average, how many cars did he sell each month last year?
    (b) For each car sold, James received $800. How much money did he receive for the cars he sold last year?

25. Brandy had 12 m of lace. After using some of it to trim her shirt, she had $4\frac{4}{5}$ m of lace left. How many meters of lace did she use?

26. 25 books are stacked together. If the thickness of each book is $\frac{3}{5}$ cm, what is the height of the pile of books?

27. There are 80 people at a party. $\frac{1}{2}$ of them are men, $\frac{1}{4}$ of the remainder are women and the rest are children. How many more adults than children are there?

28. Sean earns $2600 a month. Nicole's earnings is $\frac{4}{5}$ of Sean's. They spend $\frac{2}{3}$ of their total earnings and save the rest. How much do they save a month?

29. A bottle weighs 1.2 kg when it is $\frac{1}{4}$ filled with water. It weighs 2.4 kg when it is full. Find the weight of the empty bottle.

30. Peter and David shared $300 in the ratio 7 : 5. How much more money did Peter receive than David?

31. The ratio of the number of adults to the number of children on a ferry is 8 : 3. When 10 adults get down from the ferry, the ratio of the number of adults to the number of children becomes 2 : 1. How many children are there on the ferry?

32.  John's money is $\frac{3}{4}$ of David's money. David's money is twice as much as Paul's money.
 (a)  What is the ratio of John's money to David's money to Paul's money?
 (b)  If Paul has $60, how much money does John have?

33.  John has 40 books. Steven has 25% more books than John. How many books does Steven have?

34.  The price of a computer set was decreased from $4000 to $2800. By what percentage was the price decreased?

35.  Sam saved $500 and Alice saved $400. How many percent more did Sam save than Alice?

36.  Holly used 30% of a bag of flour for baking cakes. She used 40% of the remainder to make pizzas. What percentage of the bag of flour did she use altogether?

37.  There are 30% more boys than girls in a club. If there are 54 more boys than girls, how many children are there altogether?

38.  Mr. Wells drove from Town P to Town Q at an average speed of 60 km/h. He arrived at Town Q at 11:30 a.m. What time did he leave Town P?

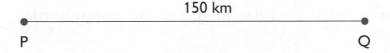

150 km

P                                                                Q

39.  A motorist traveled from Town A to Town B. He took 2 hours to cover the first $\frac{1}{2}$ of the trip at an average speed of 75 km/h. If his average speed for the whole trip was 60 km/h, find his average speed for the second $\frac{1}{2}$ of the trip.

40. Find the shaded area in the rectangle.

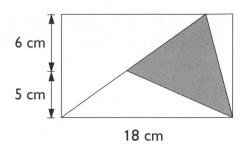

41. Copy each of the following shapes on dotted paper. Make a tessellation for each shape.

(a)

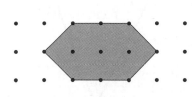

(b)

42. How many unit cubes (  ) are needed to build the following solid?

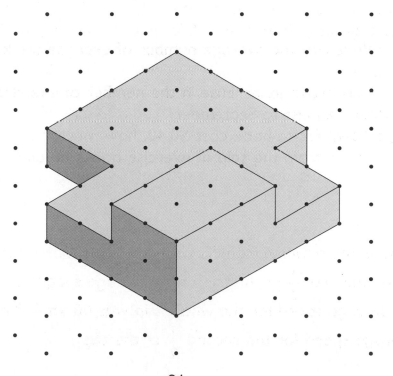

43. The line graph shows the number of exercise books sold by Mr. Ray over 4 months. Use the graph to answer the questions which follow.

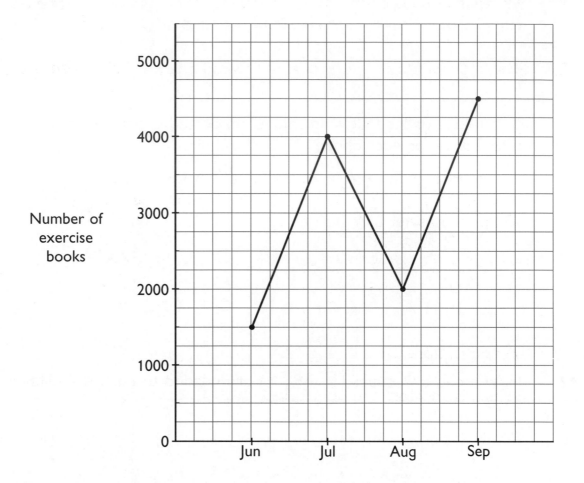

(a) What was the average number of exercise books sold per month?

(b) What was the increase in the number of exercise books sold from August to September?

(c) If an exercise book cost $0.40, how much money did Mr. Ray receive from the sale of exercise books in July?

# REVIEW F

1. Write in pounds and ounces.
   (a) 26 oz        (b) 38 oz        (c) 17 oz

2. The ratio of Mary's weight to Aly's weight is 3:4. Their total weight is 161 lb.
   (a) Find Mary's weight.
   (b) Find Aly's weight.

3. The ratio of Juan's height to his father's height is 2 : 3
   The height of Juan's father is 6 ft 3 in. Find the height of Juan.
   (Give the answer in feet and inches.)

4. Which is heavier, $3\frac{1}{4}$ lb or 50 oz?

   Which is longer, $1\frac{2}{3}$ ft or 21 in.?

   Which is more, 31 c or $2\frac{1}{2}$ gal?

   Which is shorter, $\frac{1}{3}$ yd or 15 in.?

5. Divide in compound units.

   (a) 5 yd 1 ft ÷ 2 = ▪ yd ▪ ft

   (b) 13 lb 8 oz ÷ 6 = ▪ lb ▪ oz

   (c) 19 gal 2 qt ÷ 3 = ▪ gal ▪ qt

   (d) 5 ft 10 in. ÷ 7 = ▪ ft ▪ in.

6. Mitchell ran 620 ft.
   Express 620 ft in yards and feet.

7.     What fraction of the rectangle is shaded?

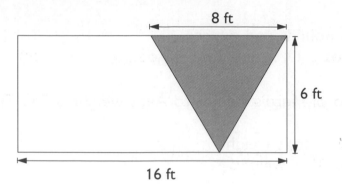

8.     (a)   $4\frac{1}{4}$ lb = ■ oz

       (b)   $2\frac{2}{3}$ yd = ■ in.

       (c)   $5\frac{1}{2}$ gal = ■ c

9.     Sally poured 15 cups of water into a jug and 3 glasses.

       She poured $\frac{3}{5}$ of the water into the jug.

       She poured the same amount of water into each of the glasses.
       How many cups of water are in each glass?

10.    Pablo bought $2\frac{1}{4}$ lb of chicken. Travis bought 43 oz of chicken.

       Who bought more chicken? How much more?
       (Give the answer in ounces.)

11.
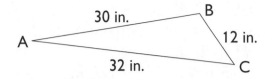

       Length of AB: Length of BC: Length of AC

       = ■ : ■ : ■

12.    Mr. Smith drove from City A to City B. The distance between the
       two cities is 300 mi. If his car can travel 15 mi per gallon of gas, how
       many gallons of gas did he use on this trip?

94

13. (a) Express 7.75 lb in pounds and ounces.

(b) Express $2\frac{5}{6}$ ft in feet and inches.

(c) Express 3.5 qt in quarts and cups.

14. What percentage of 2 ft is 6 in.?

15. Express 16 c as a percentage of 2 gal.

16. Draw a rhombus ABCD in which AB = 2 in. and ∠ BCD = 55°

17. John drove from Town A to Town B in 5 hours. His average speed for the first 3.5 hours was 65 mi/h. His average speed for the last 1.5 hours was 60 mi/h. What was the total distance he traveled?

18. The figure is made up of a rectangle and two triangles. Find the area of the figure.

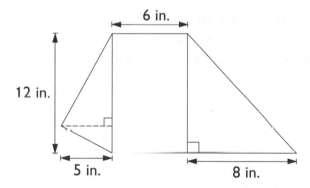

19. How many cubic feet are there in a cubic yard?

20. Which one of the following lengths is the shortest?

$3\frac{2}{3}$ yd,          11.75 ft,          122 in.

21. Adam is cycling at a speed of 8 mi/h.
How many minutes will he take to cycle 6 mi?

22. Mrs. Johnson had 3 lb 7 oz of sugar.
She used 4 oz sugar a day for 7 days. How much sugar was left?
(Give the answer in pounds and ounces.)

23. A tank is $\frac{2}{7}$ filled with water. It can hold another 3.5 gal of water. If 2.1 gal of water is added to the tank, what fraction of the tank is filled with water now?

24. A train left City A at 1:30 p.m. and arrived at City B at 5:30 p.m. It then left City B at 6:00 p.m. and arrived at City C at 9:00 p.m. If the average speed of the train for the whole trip was 85 mi/h, what was the distance between City A and City C?

25. Emily had $6\frac{2}{3}$ yd of cloth. She used 17 ft of it to make an apron. What percentage of the cloth did she use for the apron?

26. $\frac{1}{4}$ of a container holds 6 cups of water, How many cups of water does $\frac{1}{8}$ of the same container hold?

27. The rectangle, not drawn to scale, has 25% of its area shaded. The ratio of the length of the rectangle to its width is 9 : 4. What is the area of the unshaded part?

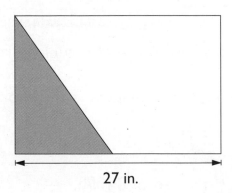

27 in.